Higher

MATHEMATICS
for OCR GCSE

Tony Banks and David Alcorn

Causeway
Press

Pearson Education Limited
Edinburgh Gate
Harlow
Essex
CM20 2JE
England

ISBN-13: 978-1-4058-3505-3
ISBN-10: 1-4058-3505-2

Exam questions
Past exam questions, provided by the *Oxford Cambridge and RSA Examinations*, are denoted by the letters OCR. The answers to all questions are entirely the responsibility of the authors/publisher and have neither been provided nor approved by OCR.

Every effort has been made to locate the copyright owners of material used in this book. Any omissions brought to the notice of the publisher are regretted and will be credited in subsequent printings.

Page design
Billy Johnson

Reader
Barbara Alcorn

Artwork
David Alcorn

Cover design
Raven Design

Typesetting by Billy Johnson, San Francisco, California, USA

Printed and bound by Scotprint, Haddington, Scotland

preface

This book provides detailed revision notes, worked examples and examination questions to support students in their preparation for the new two-tier GCSE Mathematics examinations for the OCR Specifications – Higher Tier.

The book has been designed so that it can be used in conjunction with the companion book *Higher Mathematics for OCR GCSE* or as a stand-alone revision book for self study and provides full coverage of the new OCR Specifications for the Higher Tier of entry.

In preparing the text, full account has been made of the requirements for students to be able to use and apply mathematics in written examination papers and be able to solve problems in mathematics both with and without a calculator.

The detailed revision notes, worked examples and examination questions have been organised into 40 self-contained sections which meet the requirements of the National Curriculum and provide efficient coverage of the specifications.

Sections 1 - 9	Number
Sections 10 - 22	Algebra
Sections 23 - 34	Shape, Space and Measures
Sections 35 - 40	Handling Data

At the end of the sections on Number, Algebra, Shape, Space and Measures and Handling Data, section reviews are provided to give further opportunities to consolidate skills.

At the end of the book there is a final examination questions section with a further compilation of exam and exam-style questions, organised for non-calculator and calculator practice, in preparation for the exams.

Also available *Without Answers: (ISBN: 1-405835-04-4)*
The book has been designed so that it can be used in conjunction with the companion book
Higher Mathematics for OCR GCSE (ISBN: 1-405831-45-6)

---

contents

Shape, Space and Measures

Handling Data

Whole Numbers ●●●●●●●●●

What you need to know

- You should be able to read and write numbers expressed in figures and words.
- Be able to recognise the place value of each digit in a number.

  Eg 1 In the number 5384 the digit 8 is worth 80, but in the number 4853 the digit 8 is worth 800.

- Know the Multiplication Tables up to 10×10.
- Use non-calculator methods for addition, subtraction, multiplication and division.
- Know the order of operations in a calculation.

First	Brackets and Division line
Second	Divide and Multiply
Third	Addition and Subtraction

Eg 2 $4 + 2 \times 6 = 4 + 12 = 16$

Eg 3 $9 \times (7 - 2) + 3 = 9 \times 5 + 3 = 45 + 3 = 48$

- You should be able to add, subtract, multiply and divide with negative numbers.
- Be able to use these rules with negative numbers.

| **When adding or subtracting:** |
| + + can be replaced by + |
| − − can be replaced by + |
| + − can be replaced by − |
| − + can be replaced by − |

| **When multiplying:** |
| + × + = + |
| − × − = + |
| + × − = − |
| − × + = − |

| **When dividing:** |
| + ÷ + = + |
| − ÷ − = + |
| + ÷ − = − |
| − ÷ + = − |

Eg 4 Work out.

(a) $(-5) - (-8) = -5 + 8 = 3$

(b) $(-2) \times (-3) = 6$

(c) $\dfrac{(-8) \times (+2) + (-4)}{(-5) \times (-1)} = \dfrac{-16 - 4}{5} = \dfrac{-20}{5} = -4$

Exercise 1

Do not use a calculator for this exercise.

1 (a) Write one million five thousand and ten in figures.

(b) Given that $235 \times 640 = 150\,400$, work out $1\,504\,000 \div 64$.

2 Work out. (a) $7096 + 2974$ (b) $8042 - 1357$ (c) 731×137 (d) $2002 \div 13$

3 (a) Using each of the digits 9, 2, 3 and 6 write down

(i) the largest odd number, (ii) the smallest even number.

(b) What is the answer when the smallest even number is subtracted from the largest odd number?

4 Last year Mr Alderton had the following household bills.

| Gas | £364 | Electricity | £158 | Telephone | £187 |
| Water | £244 | Insurance | £236 | Council Tax | £983 |

He paid the bills by 12 equal monthly payments.
How much was each monthly payment?

5 Calculate the cost of 24 rail tickets at £128 each.

OCR

6 Work out. (a) $2655 \div 9$ (b) 417×28 OCR

7 Naomi has collected £357 from her friends for concert tickets. The tickets cost £17 each.
How many people have paid for tickets?

8 Work out.
(a) $12 - 6 + 2$ (b) $12 \div 6 \times 2$ (c) $(27 + 8) \times 3$ (d) $\dfrac{9 - 4 + 3 \times 5}{2 \times 3 + 4}$

9 A bus started from the bus station with 30 passengers on board.
At the first stop 5 got off and some got on. At the second stop no one got off, but 6 got on.
There were then 38 passengers on the bus. How many got on at the first stop?   OCR

10 There are 232 children in Joshua's school. There are 18 more girls than boys.
How many girls are in Joshua's school?   OCR

11 A roll of wire is $500\,\text{cm}$ long.
From the roll, Debra cuts 3 pieces which each measure $75\,\text{cm}$ and 4 pieces which each measure $40\,\text{cm}$.
How much wire is left on the roll?

12 Car Hire Co. have the following cars available to rent.

Model	Corsa	Astra	Zafira
Number of cars	10	12	6
Weekly rental	£210	£255	£289

Work out the total weekly rental when all the cars are hired.

13 Calculate. (a) $\dfrac{10 \times 20 \times 30 \times 40 \times 50}{1 + 2 + 3 + 4 + 5}$ (b) $\dfrac{356 - 200 \div 25}{24}$

14 This rule can be used to estimate the temperature in °F for temperatures given in °C.

> Multiply the temperature in °C by 2 and add 30.

Use this rule to estimate -17°C in °F.

15 Work out.
(a) $(-9) - (-5) + (-3)$ (b) $\dfrac{(-7) \times (-3) - (-6)}{(-9)}$ (c) $\dfrac{(-3) \times (-5) - (-7) \times (+3)}{(-4) + (-2)}$

16 A test has 12 questions.

> A correct answer scores $+3$ marks.
> An incorrect answer scores -1 mark.

Pippa attempts every question and scores 8 marks.
How many correct answers did she get?

17 The number of bacteria in a certain colony doubles every day.
At the start of an experiment there are 96 bacteria.
How many bacteria will there be 10 days later?

18 The prizes paid out in last Saturday's Lottery are shown in the table.

Number of winners	Value of each prize
1	£6 469 676
27	£73 728
708	£1 757
41 422	£66
812 558	£10

How much was paid out in prizes in last Saturday's Lottery?

Decimals and Fractions

What you need to know

- You should be able to use non-calculator methods for addition, subtraction, multiplication and division of decimals.

  Eg 1 Work out.

  (a) 5.1×0.43

$$
\begin{array}{r}
5.1 \quad \text{(1 d.p.)} \\
\times \quad 0.43 \quad \text{(2 d.p.)} \\
\hline
153 \leftarrow 51 \times 3 \\
+2040 \leftarrow 51 \times 40 \\
\hline
2.193 \quad \text{(3 d.p.)}
\end{array}
$$

  (b) $1.64 \div 0.2$

  $\frac{1.64}{0.2} = \frac{16.4}{2} = 8.2$

  > When a number is **multiplied** by a number between 0 and 1 the result will be **smaller** than the original number.
  > When a number is **divided** by a number between 0 and 1 the result will be **larger** than the original number.

- Be able to use decimals to solve problems involving money and other measures.

- The top number of a fraction is called the **numerator**, the bottom number is called the **denominator**.

- Fractions which are equal are called **equivalent fractions**. For example, $\frac{8}{20} = \frac{4}{10} = \frac{2}{5}$

  Eg 2 Write $\frac{20}{28}$ as a fraction in its simplest form.

  $\frac{20}{28} = \frac{20 \div 4}{28 \div 4} = \frac{5}{7}$

  > Divide the numerator and denominator by the largest number that divides into both.

- $2\frac{1}{2}$ is an example of a **mixed number**. It is a mixture of whole numbers and fractions.

- $\frac{5}{2}$ is an **improper** (or '**top heavy**') fraction.

- Fractions must have the **same denominator** before **adding** or **subtracting**.

  Eg 3 Work out.

  (a) $\frac{3}{4} + \frac{2}{3} = \frac{9}{12} + \frac{8}{12} = \frac{17}{12} = 1\frac{5}{12}$

  (b) $\frac{4}{5} - \frac{1}{2} = \frac{8}{10} - \frac{5}{10} = \frac{3}{10}$

  > Add (or subtract) the numerators only. When the answer is an improper fraction change it into a mixed number.

- Mixed numbers must be changed to **improper fractions** before **multiplying** or **dividing**.

  Eg 4 Work out.

  (a) $1\frac{1}{4} \times 2\frac{1}{5} = \frac{\overset{1}{\cancel{5}}}{4} \times \frac{11}{\underset{1}{\cancel{5}}} = \frac{11}{4} = 2\frac{3}{4}$

  > The working can be simplified by cancelling.

  (b) $1\frac{1}{3} \div 1\frac{3}{5} = \frac{4}{3} \div \frac{8}{5} = \frac{\overset{1}{\cancel{4}}}{3} \times \frac{5}{\underset{2}{\cancel{8}}} = \frac{5}{6}$

  > Dividing by $\frac{8}{5}$ is the same as multiplying by $\frac{5}{8}$.

- All fractions can be written as decimals.

  > To change a fraction to a decimal divide the **numerator** by the **denominator**.

  Eg 5 Change $\frac{4}{5}$ to a decimal.

  $\frac{4}{5} = 4 \div 5 = 0.8$

- Some decimals have **recurring digits**. These are shown by:

  a single dot above a single recurring digit,

  Eg 6 $\frac{2}{3} = 0.6666\ldots = 0.\dot{6}$

  a dot above the first and last digit of a set of recurring digits.

  Eg 7 $\frac{5}{11} = 0.454545\ldots = 0.\dot{4}\dot{5}$

Do not use a calculator for questions 1 to 16.

1 (a) Lucy works out 0.2×0.4. She gets the answer 0.8.
Explain why her answer must be wrong.
(b) Work out. (i) 0.3×0.4 (ii) 0.3×0.2

2 Calculate the total cost of 16 DVDs at £14.32 each. OCR

3 Two pieces of wood of length 0.75 m and 2.68 m are sawn from a plank 5 m long.
What length of wood is left?

4 Wayne buys 2 kg of apples and 0.5 kg of cherries.
The total cost is £2.85. The apples cost 80p per kilogram.
How much per kilogram do cherries cost? OCR

5 Using the calculation $\boxed{23 \times 32 = 736}$, work out the following.
(a) 2.3×3.2 (b) $73.6 \div 23$ (c) $736 \div 3.2$

6 $5 \times m$ **gives an answer *less than* 5.** $5 \div m$ **gives an answer *more than* 5.**
Give two possible values for m which satisfy **both** conditions.

7 (a) Write down a fraction that lies halfway between $\frac{1}{3}$ and $\frac{1}{2}$.
(b) An examination is marked out of 48. Ashley scored 32 marks.
What fraction of the total did he score? Give your answer in its simplest form.

8 Calculate (a) $\frac{2}{9} \times 3$, (b) $\frac{6}{7} \div 4$.
Give your answers in their simplest form. OCR

9 The cake stall at a school fete has 200 fairy cakes for sale.
It sells $\frac{3}{5}$ of them at 25p each and the remainder at 20p each.
How much money does the stall get from selling fairy cakes?

10 George pays £1.82 for $\frac{1}{5}$ kg of toffees at £4.20 per kilogram and $\frac{1}{4}$ kg of jellies.
How much per kilogram are jellies?

11 Calculate. (a) $1\frac{2}{3} - \frac{1}{4}$ (b) $\frac{3}{5} \div \frac{2}{3}$ OCR

12 Edward, Marc, Dee and Lin share an apple pie. Edward has $\frac{1}{3}$, Marc has $\frac{1}{5}$ and Dee has $\frac{1}{4}$.
What fraction of the pie is left for Lin?

13 Work out. (a) $\frac{2}{3} + \frac{4}{5}$ (b) $2\frac{2}{5} \times \frac{5}{6}$ OCR

14 Income tax and national insurance take $\frac{1}{5}$ of Phillip's pay.
He gives $\frac{2}{5}$ of what he has left to his parents for housekeeping.
What fraction of his pay does Phillip have left for himself?

15 Three-fifths of the people at a party are boys.
Three-quarters of the boys are wearing fancy dress.
What fraction of the people at the party are boys wearing fancy dress?

16 (a) Use your calculator to change $\frac{3}{16}$ into an exact decimal.
(b) From the list of fractions, choose the fraction that is nearest to 0.5.
$$\frac{3}{7} \quad \frac{5}{9} \quad \frac{2}{5} \quad \frac{6}{11}$$
Show clear working to support your answer. OCR

17 In a sale the price of a microwave is reduced by $\frac{1}{5}$. The sale price is £96.
What was the price of the microwave before the sale?

18 Work out $\frac{12.9 \times 7.3}{3.9 + 1.4}$. Write down your full calculator display.

Approximation and Estimation

What you need to know

- How to **round** to the nearest 10, 100, 1000.

- In real-life problems a rounding must be used which gives a sensible answer.

- How to approximate using **decimal places**.

  > Write the number using one more decimal place than asked for.
  > Look at the last decimal place and
  > - if the figure is 5 or more round up,
  > - if the figure is less than 5 round down.

  Eg 1 Write the number 3.649 to
  (a) 2 decimal places,
  (b) 1 decimal place.

  (a) 3.65,
  (b) 3.6.

- How to approximate using **significant figures**.

  > Start from the most significant figure and count the required number of figures.
  > Look at the next figure to the right of this and
  > - if the figure is 5 or more round up,
  > - if the figure is less than 5 round down.
  > Add noughts, as necessary, to preserve the place value.

  Eg 2 Write each of these numbers correct to 2 significant figures.
  (a) 365
  (b) 0.0423

  (a) 370
  (b) 0.042

- You should be able to choose a suitable degree of accuracy.

  > The result of a calculation involving measurement should not be given to a greater degree of accuracy than the measurements used in the calculation.

- Be able to use approximations to estimate that the actual answer to a calculation is of the right order of magnitude.

  > Estimation is done by approximating every number in the calculation to one significant figure.
  > The calculation is then done using the approximated values.

  Eg 3 Use approximations to estimate $\dfrac{5.1 \times 57.2}{9.8}$.

  $$\frac{5.1 \times 57.2}{9.8} = \frac{5 \times 60}{10} = 30$$

- Be able to use a calculator to check answers to calculations.

- Be able to recognise limitations on the accuracy of data and measurements.

  Eg 4 Jamie said, "I have 60 friends at my party." This figure is correct to the nearest 10. What is the smallest and largest possible number of friends Jamie had at his party?

  The smallest whole number that rounds to 60 is 55.
  The largest whole number that rounds to 60 is 64.
  So, smallest is 55 friends and largest is 64 friends.

  Eg 5 A man weighs 57 kg, correct to the nearest kilogram. What is the minimum weight of the man?
  Minimum weight = 57 kg − 0.5 kg = 56.5 kg.

  Eg 6 Calculate the upper bound of $\dfrac{a}{b}$ when:
  $a = 7.6$, correct to 2 sig. figs., and $b = 50$, correct to 2 sig. figs.

  $$\text{Upper bound of } \frac{a}{b} = \frac{\text{upper bound of } a}{\text{lower bound of } b} = \frac{7.6 + 0.05}{50 - 0.5} = \frac{7.65}{49.5} = 0.154545\ldots$$

1 Write the result shown on the calculator display
  (a) to the nearest ten,
  (b) correct to one decimal place,
  (c) correct to one significant figure.

2 A newspaper's headline states: "20 000 people attend concert".
  The number in the newspaper is given to the nearest thousand.
  What is the smallest possible attendance?

3 On Saturday a dairy sold 2975 litres of milk at 42 pence per litre.
  By rounding each number to one significant figure, estimate the amount of money received
  from the sale of milk, giving your answer in pounds.

4 (a) A group of 17 people win £59 372 in a lottery.
      They share the money equally between them.
      Estimate how much money they will each receive.
      Show how you worked out your estimate.
  (b) Work out an **estimate** for the value of $\dfrac{51 \times 38}{0.47}$.
      Show how you worked out your estimate.   OCR

5 Mrs Patel is buying some history books. The books cost £6.95 each.
  She wants to estimate the cost of 39 books.
  (a) Write down a calculation she could do in her head to work out an estimate for the
      total cost.
  (b) Is her estimate bigger or smaller than the exact cost? Explain how you decided.   OCR

6 A car park has spaces for 640 cars, correct to the nearest ten.
  What is the greatest possible number of spaces in the car park?

7 In 2005, Mr Symms drove 8873 kilometres.
  His car does 11 kilometres per litre. Petrol costs 89.9 pence per litre.
  (a) By rounding each number to one significant figure, estimate the amount he spent
      on petrol.
  (b) Without any further calculation, explain why this estimate will be larger than the
      actual amount.

8 Andrew says, "Answers given to two decimal places are more accurate than answers given
  to two significant figures." Is he right? Explain your answer.

9 Calculate the value of $\dfrac{65.4}{4.3 + 3.58}$.
  (a) Write down your full calculator display.
  (b) Give your answer correct to 3 significant figures.

10 Calculate. $\dfrac{6.5 \times 4.7}{6.7 - 1.9}$ Give your answer correct to 1 decimal place.   OCR

11 (a) Calculate $\dfrac{50 - 19.7}{31.6 + 55.1}$. Give your answer correct to two decimal places.
   (b) By using approximations, show that your answer to (a) is about right.
       You **must** show all your working.

12 A school orders 20 copies of a book. Each book weighs 0.46 kg, correct to 2 decimal places.
   Calculate the lower bound and the upper bound of the total weight of the books.

13 The magnification of a lens is given by the formula $m = \dfrac{v}{u}$.
   In an experiment, u is measured as 8.5 cm and v is measured as 14.0 cm, both correct to the
   nearest 0.1 cm.
   Find the least possible value of m.   OCR

Percentages and Money

What you need to know

- 10% is read as '10 percent'. 'Per cent' means out of 100. 10% means 10 out of 100.

- A percentage can be written as a fraction, 10% can be written as $\frac{10}{100}$.

- To change a decimal or a fraction to a percentage: **multiply by 100**.

- To change a percentage to a fraction or a decimal: **divide by 100**.

- How to express one quantity as a percentage of another.

  Eg 1 Write 30p as a percentage of £2.
  $\frac{30}{200} \times 100 = 30 \times 100 \div 200 = 15\%$

  > Write the numbers as a fraction, using the same units.
  > Change the fraction to a percentage.

- You should be able to use percentages to solve a variety of problems.

- Be able to find a percentage of a quantity.

  Eg 2 Find 20% of £64.
  £64 ÷ 100 = £0.64
  £0.64 × 20 = £12.80

  > 1. Divide by 100 to find 1%.
  > 2. Multiply by the percentage to be found.

- Be able to find a percentage increase (or decrease).

  $$\text{Percentage increase} = \frac{\text{actual increase}}{\text{initial value}} \times 100\%$$
  $$\text{Percentage decrease} = \frac{\text{actual decrease}}{\text{initial value}} \times 100\%$$

  Eg 3 Find the percentage loss on a micro-scooter bought for £25 and sold for £18.
  Percentage loss $= \frac{7}{25} \times 100 = 28\%$

- Be able to solve reverse percentage problems.

  Eg 4 Find the original price of a car which is sold at a loss of 20% for £1200.

  80% of original price = £1200
  1% of original price = £1200 ÷ 80 = £15
  Original price = £15 × 100 = £1500

  > First find 1% of the original value by dividing the selling price by (100 − % loss), then multiply by 100.

- **Hourly pay** is paid at a **basic rate** for a fixed number of hours.
  Overtime pay is usually paid at a higher rate such as time and a half, which means each hour's work is worth 1.5 times the basic rate.

- Everyone is allowed to earn some money which is not taxed. This is called a **tax allowance**.

- Tax is only paid on income earned in excess of the tax allowance. This is called **taxable income**.

  Eg 5 Tom earns £6080 per year.
  His tax allowance is £4895 per year and he pays tax at 10p in the £ on his taxable income.
  Find how much income tax Tom pays per year.

  Taxable income   = £6080 − £4895 = £1185
  Income tax payable = £1185 × 0.10 = £118.50

  > First find the taxable income, then multiply taxable income by rate in £.

- **Value added tax**, or **VAT**, is a tax on some goods and services and is added to the bill.

- When considering a **best buy**, compare quantities by using the same units.
  For example, find which product gives more grams per penny.

- Money invested in a savings account at a bank or building society earns **interest**.
- With **Simple Interest**, the interest is paid out each year and not added to your account.

$$\text{Simple Interest} = \frac{\text{Amount}}{\text{invested}} \times \frac{\text{Time in}}{\text{years}} \times \frac{\text{Rate of interest}}{\text{per year}}$$

Eg 6 Find the Simple Interest paid on £600 invested for 6 months at 8% per year.

Simple Interest $= 600 \times \frac{6}{12} \times \frac{8}{100} = 600 \times 0.5 \times 0.08 = £24$

- With **Compound Interest**, the interest earned each year is added to your account and also earns interest the following year.

Eg 7 Find the **Compound Interest** paid on £600 invested for 2 years at 6% per year.

1st year
Investment	= £600
Interest: £600 × 0.06	= £ 36
Value after one year	= £636

2nd year
Investment	= £636
Interest: £636 × 0.06	= £ 38.16
Value after two years	= £674.16

Compound Interest = Final value − Original value = £674.16 − £600 = £74.16

This could be calculated as: $600 \times (1.06)^2 - 600 = £74.16$

Exercise 4

Do not use a calculator for questions 1 to 5.

1 What is 40 as a percentage of 500?

2 A test is marked out of 80. Colin scored 35% of the marks.
How many marks did Colin score?

3 A jacket normally costs £48. The price is reduced by 15% in a sale.
What is the price of the jacket in the sale?

4 A market trader buys 25 kg of apples at 40p per kg.
She makes 70% profit on the first 20 kg of apples that she sells.
The rest she sells at only $\frac{4}{5}$ of what she paid for them.
How much profit does she make?   OCR

5 Angela is paid £7.40 per hour for a basic 35-hour week. Overtime is paid at time and a half.
Last week Angela was paid £303.40.
How many hours did she work last week?

6 Mrs Tilsed wishes to buy a car priced at £2400.

> **Two options are available.**
> **Option 1** – A deposit of 20% of £2400 and 24 monthly payments of £95.
> **Option 2** – For a single payment the dealer offers a discount of 5% on £2400.

£2400

How much more does it cost to buy the car if option 1 is chosen rather than option 2?

7 Paul wants to buy a new computer.
At *PC Essentials*, Paul needs to pay £890 plus VAT at $17\frac{1}{2}$%.
At *Computers For All*, the total price is £999.
Find the difference in the price of the computers.   OCR

8 Toffee is sold in bars of two sizes.
A large bar weighs 450 g and costs £1.69. A small bar weighs 275 g and costs 99p.
Which size of bar is better value for money? You must show all your working.

9 A farmer has 200 sheep. 90% of the sheep have lambs.
Of the sheep which have lambs 45% have two lambs.
How many of the sheep have two lambs?

10 Lily invests £1000 at 4.25% per annum simple interest.
She withdraws her money after 6 months.
How much interest did she get?

11 Last year Leroy had a tax allowance of £4895 and paid £3520 in tax.
How much did Leroy earn last year if he paid tax at the rate of 10p in the £ on the first £2090 of his taxable income and 22p in the £ on all his remaining income?

12 The volume of a block of ice is 19 700 cm³.
When placed in a warm room, the ice melts. During each hour the volume of the block reduces by 15% of its volume at the beginning of the hour.
Calculate the volume of ice **remaining** after 2 hours.
Give your answer to a suitable degree of accuracy.

OCR

13

1st STOP Car Insurance

Typical insurance:
Vauxhall Corsa - £650 per year
No Claims Discount Available

(a) Vanessa has a Vauxhall Corsa. She is given a no claims discount.
After taking off her no claims discount she has to pay £390 to insure her car.
Calculate her no claims discount as a percentage of £650.
(b) Cedric has a BMW car. He is given a 65% no claims discount.
After the discount he has to pay £336 to insure his car.
Calculate the price of the insurance before the discount.

14 A jeweller's shop has a closing down sale.
(a) Each morning a ring is reduced by 20% of the previous day's price until it is sold.
Monday's price was £150. The ring had not been sold by Wednesday morning.
What was the price of the ring on Wednesday?
(b) All necklaces have been reduced by 30%. One necklace is on sale for £147.
What was its price before the reduction?

OCR

15 This report appeared in a motoring magazine.

> In the first year of ownership a new car loses 20% of its value and in the second year it loses 15% of its one-year old value.

If this report is true, what is the percentage loss in the value of a new car in its first 2 years?

16 Questionnaires were sent to a number of people. 72 people replied.
This was only 18% of all the people that had been sent questionnaires.
How many people had been sent questionnaires?

17 In 2002 Quentin bought an antique table for £7500.
The next year the value of the table increased by 6%.
In each of the following 2 years the value of the table increased by 8% of its value in the previous year.
What was the value of the table when Quentin sold it in 2005?

OCR

18 (a) Mike invests £3000 at 5% per annum compound interest.
What is the value of his investment after 3 years?
(b) Jayne invests her money at 6% per annum compound interest.
What is the percentage increase in the value of her investment after 3 years?

Working with Number

What you need to know

- **Multiples** of a number are found by multiplying the number by 1, 2, 3, 4, …

  Eg 1 The multiples of 8 are $1 \times 8 = 8$, $2 \times 8 = 16$, $3 \times 8 = 24$, $4 \times 8 = 32$, …

- **Factors** of a number are found by listing all the products that give the number.

  Eg 2 $1 \times 6 = 6$ and $2 \times 3 = 6$. So, the factors of 6 are: 1, 2, 3 and 6.

- The **common factors** of two numbers are the numbers which are factors of **both**.

- A **prime number** is a number with only two factors, 1 and the number itself.
  The first few prime numbers are: 2, 3, 5, 7, 11, 13, 17, 19, …
  The number 1 is not a prime number because it has only one factor.

- The **prime factors** of a number are those factors of the number which are prime numbers.

  Eg 3 The factors of 18 are: 1, 2, 3, 6, 9 and 18.
  The prime factors of 18 are: 2 and 3.

- The **Least Common Multiple** of two numbers is the smallest number that is a multiple of both.

  Eg 4 The Least Common Multiple of 4 and 5 is 20.

- The **Highest Common Factor** of two numbers is the largest number that is a factor of both.

  Eg 5 The Highest Common Factor of 8 and 12 is 4.

- An expression such as $3 \times 3 \times 3 \times 3 \times 3$ can be written in a shorthand way as 3^5.
  This is read as '3 to the power of 5'.
  The number 3 is the **base** of the expression. 5 is the **power**.

- Powers can be used to help write any number as the **product of its prime factors**.

  Eg 6 $72 = 2 \times 2 \times 2 \times 3 \times 3 = 2^3 \times 3^2$

- Numbers raised to the power of 2 are **squared**.

  Squares can be calculated using the $\boxed{x^2}$ button on a calculator.

  > **Square numbers** are whole numbers squared.
  > The first few square numbers are: 1, 4, 9, 16, 25, 36, …

  The opposite of squaring a number is called finding the **square root**.

  Square roots can be calculated using the $\boxed{\sqrt{\ }}$ button on a calculator.

  The square root of a number can be positive or negative.

  Eg 7 The square root of 9 can be written as $\sqrt{9}$ or $9^{\frac{1}{2}}$, and is equal to $+3$ or -3.

- Numbers raised to the power of 3 are **cubed**.

  > **Cube numbers** are whole numbers cubed.
  > The first few cube numbers are: 1, 8, 27, 64, 125, …

  The opposite of cubing a number is called finding the **cube root**.

  Cube roots can be calculated using the $\boxed{\sqrt[3]{\ }}$ button on a calculator.

  Eg 8 The cube root of 27 can be written as $\sqrt[3]{27}$ or $27^{\frac{1}{3}}$, and is equal to 3.

● **Powers**

The squares and cubes of numbers can be worked out on a calculator by using the $\boxed{x^y}$ button.
The $\boxed{x^y}$ button can be used to calculate the value of a number x raised to the power of y.

Eg 9 Calculate 2.6^4.
Enter the sequence: $\boxed{2}$ $\boxed{\cdot}$ $\boxed{6}$ $\boxed{x^y}$ $\boxed{4}$ $\boxed{=}$ So, $2.6^4 = 45.6976$.

● The **reciprocal** of a number is the value obtained when the number is divided into 1.
The reciprocal of a number can be found on
a calculator by using the $\boxed{\frac{1}{x}}$ button.

A number times its reciprocal equals 1.
Zero has no reciprocal.
The reciprocal of a number can be
shown using an index of -1.

Eg 10 Find the reciprocal of 5.
The reciprocal of $5 = 5^{-1} = \frac{1}{5} = 0.2$

Using a calculator, press: $\boxed{5}$ $\boxed{\frac{1}{x}}$

● **Roots** can be calculated using the $\boxed{x^{1/y}}$ button.

Eg 11 Calculate $\sqrt[7]{128}$.
Enter the sequence: $\boxed{1}$ $\boxed{2}$ $\boxed{8}$ $\boxed{x^{1/y}}$ $\boxed{7}$ $\boxed{=}$ So, $\sqrt[7]{128} = 2$.

● **The rules of indices**

Multiplying powers with the same base	$a^m \times a^n = a^{m+n}$
Dividing powers with the same base	$a^m \div a^n = a^{m-n}$
Raising a power to a power	$(a^m)^n = a^{mn}$
Raising any number to the power zero	$a^0 = 1$ (also $a^1 = a$)
Negative powers and reciprocals	$a^{-m} = \dfrac{1}{a^m}$ a^{-m} is the reciprocal of a^m
Fractional powers and roots	$a^{\frac{1}{n}} = \sqrt[n]{a}$ and $a^{\frac{m}{n}} = \left(a^{\frac{1}{n}}\right)^m = \left(\sqrt[n]{a}\right)^m$

Eg 12 Simplify. Leave your answers in index form.
(a) $2^9 \times 2^4 = 2^{9+4} = 2^{13}$ (b) $2^9 \div 2^4 = 2^{9-4} = 2^5$ (c) $(4^9)^3 = 4^{9 \times 3} = 4^{27}$

● You should be able to use the function keys on a calculator to solve a variety of problems.

Exercise 5   Do not use a calculator for questions 1 to 20.

1 (a) Write down all the factors of 18.
(b) Write down a multiple of 7 between 30 and 40.
(c) Explain why 15 is not a prime number.

2 Work out the value of (a) 4^2,   (b) 5^3,   (c) 10^4,   (d) 2.5×10^6.

3 Work out the following.
(a) the cube of 3   (b) 2^4 (c) 0.3^2 (d) an **estimate** of 8.8^2 OCR

4 Richard says that $1^3 + 2^3 = 3^3$.
Is he right? Show your working.

5 Use examples to show that the sum of the squares of two prime numbers can be odd or even.

6 Find the value of (a) $1^2 + 2^2 + 3^2 + 4^2 + 5^2$,   (b) $9^2 \times 10^2$,   (c) $2^3 \times 5^2$.

7 (a) Work out. (i) 10^3 (ii) $\frac{2^5}{4^2}$ (iii) 0.6^2
(b)   21   22   23   24   25   26   27   28   29
From these numbers, choose one which is:
(i) a cube number,   (ii) a prime number.   OCR

8 Work out.   (a) $2^3 \times 3^2$ (b) $\sqrt{25} + \sqrt{144}$ (c) $\sqrt{49} \times 4^2$

9 (a) Simplify. $\dfrac{7^2 \times 7^3}{7^6}$

    (b) Write down $\sqrt{169}$.

    (c) Write 120 as a product of its prime factors.   OCR

10 (a) Write 36 as a product of its prime factors.

    (b) Write 45 as a product of its prime factors.

    (c) What is the highest common factor of 36 and 45?

    (d) What is the least common multiple of 36 and 45?

11 Find the highest common factor (HCF) of 12 and 20.   OCR

12 A white light flashes every 10 seconds.
A red light flashes every 6 seconds.
The two lights flash at the same time.
After how many seconds will the lights next flash at the same time?

13 Work out.   (a) $\sqrt{2^4 \times 3^2}$ (b) $\left(\sqrt{9} \times \sqrt{25}\right)^2$ (c) $2^3 \times \sqrt[3]{64}$

14 (a) Which is smaller $\sqrt{225}$ or 2^4? Show your working.

    (b) Work out the value of $3^1 - 3^0 + 3^{-1}$.

15 Find the value of x in each of the following.

    (a) $7^6 \times 7^3 = 7^x$ (b) $7^6 \div 7^3 = 7^x$ (c) $(7^6)^3 = 7^x$ (d) $7^0 = x$

16 Simplify fully each of these expressions. Leave your answers in power form.

    (a) $3^2 \times 3^3$ (b) $4^{-2} \times 4^5$ (c) $5^6 \div 5^3$ (d) $9^4 \div 9^{-2}$ (e) $\dfrac{2^3 \times 2}{2^6}$

17 (a) Write 6.4×10^3 as an ordinary number.

    (b) Find the value of n in each of the following.

       (i) $0.0002 = 2 \times 10^n$ (ii) $4^n = 1$ (iii) $\dfrac{1}{25} = 5^n$ OCR

18 Evaluate: (a) $9^{\frac{1}{2}}$ (b) $64^{-\frac{1}{2}}$ (c) $25^{\frac{3}{2}}$ (d) $16^{-\frac{3}{4}}$

19 Evaluate: $81^{0.5} \times 5^{-2}$. Give your answer as a fraction.

20 Simplify, leaving your answers in fractional form.

    (a) $64^{\frac{1}{2}} \times 125^{-\frac{1}{3}}$ (b) $27^{\frac{2}{3}} \times 3^{-4}$ (c) $\left(\frac{1}{2}\right)^{-3} \div \left(\frac{1}{5}\right)^{-2}$

21 (a) Find the reciprocal of 7, correct to two decimal places.

    (b) Find the value of 5.6^3.

22 Calculate $\dfrac{3.82^2}{3.41 - 1.25}$. Give your answer correct to 2 decimal places.   OCR

23 Calculate the following.   (a) $\dfrac{87.2}{46.1 - 19.4}$ (b) $\dfrac{4.8 \times \sqrt{31.44}}{\sqrt{7.86}}$ OCR

24 Calculate. $2.5^3 - 1.6^2 \times 4.75$ OCR

25 (a) Calculate the value of $\sqrt{\dfrac{4.1}{(0.19)^2}}$.

    (b) Show how to check that your answer is of the right order of magnitude.

26 Calculate the value of:

    (a) $5^{\frac{2}{5}}$ (b) $\dfrac{1}{(0.7)^5}$ (c) $\sqrt[3]{\dfrac{920\,000}{5^4}}$ (d) $\left(\dfrac{5.9}{\sqrt[3]{15}}\right)^{-3}$

Give your answers correct to two significant figures.

Standard Index Form ●●●●●

What you need to know

- **Standard index form**, or **standard form**, is a shorthand way of writing very large and very small numbers.

- In **standard form** a number is written as: **a number between 1 and 10 × a power of 10**. Large numbers (ten, or more) have a **positive** power of 10.

  Eg 1　Write　370 000　in standard form.
  $370\,000 = 3.7 \times 100\,000 = 3.7 \times 10^5$

  Eg 2　Write　5.6×10^7　as an ordinary number.
  $5.6 \times 10^7 = 5.6 \times 10\,000\,000 = 56\,000\,000$

  Small positive numbers (less than one) have a **negative** power of 10.

  Eg 3　Write　0.000 73　in standard form.
  $0.000\,73 = 7.3 \times 0.000\,1 = 7.3 \times 10^{-4}$

  Eg 4　Write　2.9×10^{-6}　as an ordinary number.
  $2.9 \times 10^{-6} = 2.9 \times 0.000\,001 = 0.000\,002\,9$

- You should be able to interpret the display on a calculator.

  Eg 5　The calculator display shows the answer to　0.007×0.09
  In standard form, the answer is　6.3×10^{-4}
  As an ordinary number, the answer is　0.000 63

6.3 $\quad$ -04

- You should be able to solve problems involving numbers given in standard form.

Exercise 6　　Do not use a calculator for questions 1 to 9.

1　Write　one million　in standard form.

2　Here is a list of numbers written in standard form.

$$8.36 \times 10^2 \qquad 3.9 \times 10^3 \qquad 5.7 \times 10^{-3}$$
$$9.22 \times 10^{-1} \qquad 1.31 \times 10^4 \qquad 6.15 \times 10^{-2}$$

Write, as ordinary numbers, the largest and smallest numbers in the list.　　OCR

3　Write in standard index form.　(a)　57 000 000　　　(b)　0.000 057

4　(a)　Write　9.2×10^7　as an ordinary number.
　　(b)　A sheet of paper is 6.1×10^{-2} mm thick.
　　　　What is the total thickness of five sheets of this paper?
　　　　Give your answer in standard form.　　OCR

5　(a)　Write　0.00013　in standard form.
　　(b)　Write　3.14×10^7　as an ordinary number.
　　(c)　Work out　$2.5 \times 10^3 + 1.25 \times 10^4$.
　　　　Give your answer in standard form.　　OCR

6　Work out.
　　(a)　$(6 \times 10^3) + (5 \times 10^4)$
　　(b)　$(6 \times 10^3) \times (5 \times 10^4)$
　　(c)　$(6 \times 10^3) \div (5 \times 10^4)$
　　Give your answers in standard form.

7 The table shows the populations of four countries in Latin America.

Country	Population
Belize	2.0×10^5
Guatemala	1.2×10^7
Mexico	1.1×10^8
Nicaragua	4.9×10^6

(a) Which of these countries has the largest population?
(b) How many more people live in Nicaragua than in Belize?
(c) What is the total population of these four countries?
    Give your answer in standard form.

8 (a) The diameter of an asteroid is 13 km, correct to the nearest kilometre.
    Between what limits does the actual diameter lie?

Sun   Earth   Mars

(b) Mars is 228 000 000 km from the Sun.
    Write 228 000 000 in standard form.
(c) The Earth is 1.5×10^8 km from the Sun.
    Light travels at 3×10^5 km per second.
    How many seconds does it take light to travel from the Sun to the Earth?   OCR

9 (a) Write 0.000 006 in standard form.

(b) Work out $\dfrac{3 \times 10^4}{5 \times 10^{-5}}$, giving your answer in standard form.

10 Last Sunday 1.85 million copies of a newspaper were printed.
Each of these newspapers weighed 234 grams.
Calculate the total weight of these newspapers in kilograms.
Give your answer in standard form.

11 (a) Calculate $\dfrac{7.2 \times 10^6}{0.0045}$.

    Give your answer in standard form.

(b) Calculate $\dfrac{530}{6.7 \times 10^5}$.

    Give your answer as an ordinary number correct to two significant figures.

12 In Astronomy, the distance between stars is measured in light years.
A light year is approximately 9.46×10^{12} kilometres.
Alpha Cygni is approximately 1.05×10^{14} kilometres from the Sun.
How many light years is Alpha Cygni from the Sun?

13 Work out $\dfrac{3.5 \times 10^{-3}}{4.1 \times 10^2}$.

Give your answer as an ordinary number correct to 2 significant figures.

14 Work out $\dfrac{(3.5 \times 10^6) \times (5 \times 10^{-4})}{2.5 \times 10^5}$. Give your answer as an ordinary number.

15 (a) Write 0.0004 in standard form.

(b) Work out $\dfrac{(2.45 \times 10^5) \times (6 \times 10^4)}{1.5 \times 10^{-2}}$. Give your answer in standard form.   OCR

Ratio and Proportion

What you need to know

- The ratio 3 : 2 is read '3 to 2'.

- A ratio is used only to **compare** quantities.
  A ratio does not give information about the exact values of quantities being compared.

- In its **simplest form**, a ratio contains whole numbers which have no common factor other than 1.

  Eg 1 Write £2.40 : 40p in its simplest form.
  £2.40 : 40p = 240p : 40p
  $\qquad\qquad\quad$ = 240 : 40
  $\qquad\qquad\quad$ = 6 : 1

  > All quantities in a ratio must be in the **same units** before the ratio can be simplified.

- You should be able to solve a variety of problems involving ratio.

  Eg 2 The ratio of bats to balls in a box is 3 : 5.
  There are 12 bats in the box.
  How many balls are there?

  12 ÷ 3 = 4
  3 × 4 : 5 × 4 = 12 : 20
  There are 20 balls in the box.

  > For every 3 bats there are 5 balls.
  > To find an **equivalent ratio** to 3 : 5, in which the first number is 12, multiply each number in the ratio by 4.

  Eg 3 A wall costs £660 to build.
  The costs of materials to labour are in the ratio 4 : 7.
  What is the cost of labour?

  4 + 7 = 11
  £660 ÷ 11 = £60
  Cost of labour = £60 × 7 = £420

  > The numbers in the ratio add to 11.
  > For every £11 of the total cost, £4 pays for materials and £7 pays for labour.
  > So, **divide** by 11 and then **multiply** by 7.

- When two different quantities are always in the **same ratio** the two quantities are in **direct proportion**.

  Eg 4 20 litres of petrol cost £14.
  Find the cost of 25 litres of petrol.

  20 litres cost £14
  1 litre costs £14 ÷ 20 = £0.70
  25 litres cost £0.70 × 25 = £17.50

  > This is sometimes called the **unitary method**.
  > **Divide** by 20 to find the cost of 1 litre.
  > **Multiply** by 25 to find the cost of 25 litres.

- When as one quantity increases the other decreases, the quantities are in **inverse proportion**.

  Eg 5 3 people take 8 hours to deliver some leaflets.
  How long would it take 4 people?

  3 people take 8 hours.
  1 person takes 8 hours × 3 = 24 hours
  4 people take 24 hours ÷ 4 = 6 hours
  So, 4 people would take 6 hours.

  > This assumes that time is **inversely proportional** to the number of people.
  > **Multiply** by 3 to find how long 1 person would take.
  > **Divide** by 4 to find how long 4 people would take.

Exercise 7

Do not use a calculator for questions 1 to 6.

1 A toy box contains large bricks and small bricks in the ratio 1 : 4.
The box contains 40 bricks. How many large bricks are in the box?

2 Amy and Brett buy a present for their mother. They share the cost in the ratio 3 : 1.
What percentage of the cost does Amy pay?   OCR

3 Two girls, Erica and Sonia, shared £30 between them in the ratio 1 to 5.
How much did Sonia receive?   OCR

4 Naheed is given £4. She spends £3.20 and saves the rest.
Express the amount she spends to the amount she saves as a ratio in its simplest form.

5 Dec shares a prize of £435 with Annabel in the ratio 3 : 2.
What is the difference in the amount of money they each receive?

6 The ratio of men to women playing golf one day is 7 : 3.
(a)   What percentage of the people playing golf are men?
(b)   There are 21 men playing.
      How many women are playing?

7 A recipe for fish pie includes these ingredients.

| 800 g white fish | 120 g prawns | 900 g potatoes | 150 ml soured cream |

(a)   Richard has 1000 g of white fish. He uses it all the make a larger pie with the recipe.
      What weight of prawns should he use?
(b)   Judy has 600 g of potatoes. She uses them to make a smaller pie with the recipe.
      What quantity of soured cream should she use?   OCR

8 3 kg of pears cost £2.94.
How much will 2 kg of pears cost?

9 Two students are talking about their school outing.

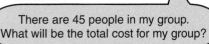
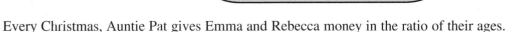

My class went to Tower Bridge last week.
There are 30 people in my class.
The total cost was £345.

There are 45 people in my group.
What will be the total cost for my group?

10 Every Christmas, Auntie Pat gives Emma and Rebecca money in the ratio of their ages.
(a)   One year, Emma was 5 years old and Rebecca was 3 years old.
      That year, Emma received £40.
      How much did Rebecca receive?
(b)   The next year, the girls received £90 to share to share between them.
      How much did each girl receive?   OCR

11 A farmer estimates it will take 2 combine harvesters 6 days to harvest his crop.
Estimate how many days it will take 3 combine harvesters to harvest his crop.

12 When petrol is 80 pence a litre it costs £28.80 to fill the tank of my car with petrol.
How much will it cost to fill the tank of my car with petrol when petrol is 90 pence per litre?

13 On a map the distance between two towns is 5 cm.
The actual distance between the towns is 1 kilometre.
What is the scale of the map in the form of 1 : *n*?

14 Tim, Shula and Carol share the running costs of a car in the ratio 1 : 2 : 3.
Last year, it cost £1860 to run the car.
How much did Carol pay?   OCR

15 At 80 km/h it takes 30 minutes to complete a journey.
How long would it take to complete the journey at 50 km/h?

Speed and Other Compound Measures

What you need to know

- **Speed** is a compound measure because it involves **two** other measures.

- **Speed** is a measurement of how fast something is travelling.
  It involves two other measures, **distance** and **time**.
  In situations where speed is not constant, **average speed** is used.

  > The formula linking speed, distance and time can be rearranged and remembered as:
  > $$S = D \div T$$
  > $$D = S \times T$$
  > $$T = D \div S$$

  $$\text{Speed} = \frac{\text{Distance}}{\text{Time}} \qquad \text{Average speed} = \frac{\text{Total distance travelled}}{\text{Total time taken}}$$

- You should be able to solve problems involving speed, distance and time.

  Eg 1 A greyhound takes 32 seconds to run 400 metres.
  Calculate its speed in metres per second.

  $$\text{Speed} = \frac{\text{Distance}}{\text{Time}} = \frac{400}{32} = 12.5 \text{ metres per second}$$

  Eg 2 Norrie says, "If I drive at an average speed of 60 km/h it will take me $2\frac{1}{2}$ hours to complete my journey." What distance is his journey?

  $$\text{Distance} = \text{Speed} \times \text{Time} = 60 \times 2\frac{1}{2} = 150 \text{ km}$$

  Eg 3 Ellen cycles 5 km at an average speed of 12 km/h.
  How many minutes does she take?

  > To change hours to minutes:
  > **multiply by 60**

  $$\text{Time} = \frac{\text{Distance}}{\text{Speed}} = \frac{5}{12} \text{ hours} = \frac{5}{12} \times 60 = 25 \text{ minutes}$$

- **Density** is a compound measure which involves the measures **mass** and **volume**.

  Eg 4 A block of metal has mass 500 g and volume 400 cm³.

  $$\text{Density} = \frac{\text{Mass}}{\text{Volume}} = \frac{500}{400} = 1.25 \text{ g/cm}^3$$

  > $$\text{Density} = \frac{\text{Mass}}{\text{Volume}}$$

- **Population density** is a measure of how populated an area is.

  Eg 5 The population of Cumbria is 489 700.
  The area of Cumbria is 6824 km².

  > $$\text{Population density} = \frac{\text{Population}}{\text{Area}}$$

  $$\text{Population density} = \frac{\text{Population}}{\text{Area}} = \frac{489\,700}{6824} = 71.8 \text{ people/km}^2.$$

Exercise 8

Do not use a calculator for questions 1 to 5.

1 Sean cycled 24 km at an average speed of 16 km/h.
How long did he take to complete the journey?

2 Ahmed takes $2\frac{1}{2}$ hours to drive from New Milton to London.
He averages 66 km/h.
What distance does he drive?

3 A motorist travels a distance of 156 miles in $3\frac{1}{4}$ hours.
Calculate the average speed of the motorist in miles per hour.

4 Kay walks 2.7 km in 45 minutes.
Calculate her average walking speed in kilometres per hour.

5 (a) Keith drives to Birmingham on a motorway.
He travels 150 miles in 2 hours 30 minutes. Work out his average speed.
(b) He drives to Cambridge at an average speed of 57 mph.
The journey takes 3 hours 20 minutes. How many miles is the journey?   OCR

6 The diagram shows the distances, in miles, between some junctions on a motorway.

A coach is travelling west. At 1040 it passes junction 27 and at 1052 it passes junction 26.
(a) Calculate the average speed of the coach in miles per hour.

Between junctions 26 and 25 the coach travels at an average speed of 30 miles per hour.
(b) Calculate the time when the coach passes junction 25.

7 Anna drove 35 miles from Southampton to Basingstoke.
She drove at an average speed of 20 mph for the first 5 miles and then at an average speed of 60 mph for the remaining 30 miles.
Calculate her average speed for the whole journey.   OCR

8 A train travels at an average speed of 80 miles per hour.
At 0940 the train is 65 miles from Glasgow. The train is due to arrive in Glasgow at 1030.
Will it arrive on time? Show your working.

9 A horse gallops at an average speed of 24 km/h for $4\frac{1}{2}$ minutes.
Calculate the distance it travels.

10 On Monday it took Helen 40 minutes to drive to work.
On Tuesday it took Helen 25 minutes to drive to work.
Her average speed on Monday was 18 miles per hour.
What was her average speed on Tuesday?

11 On a journey, Carol drove the first 90 miles. Her average speed was 60 mph.
(a) For how long did Carol drive?
(b) Tim drove the remaining 85 miles in 2 hours.
Calculate the average speed for their whole journey.   OCR

12 Rhys completed a 400 m race in 64 seconds.
Calculate his average speed in kilometres per hour.

13 A jet-ski travels 0.9 kilometres in 1.5 minutes.
Calculate the average speed of the jet-ski in metres per second.

14 The distance from the Earth to the Moon is 3.81×10^5 kilometres.
Light travels at a speed of 3×10^8 metres per second.
How long does it take light to travel from the Earth to the Moon?

15 (a) A goods train, 150 metres long, is travelling at 45 km/h.
How many seconds does it take to pass a signal?
(b) The goods train takes 5 seconds to pass a passenger train, 90 metres long,
travelling in the opposite direction.
Calculate the speed of the passenger train in kilometres per hour.

16 A copper statue has a mass of 1080 g and a volume of 120 cm³.
Work out the density of copper.

17 A silver medal has a mass of 200 g. The density of silver is 10.5 g/cm³.
What is the volume of the medal?

18 The population of Jamaica is 2.8 million people. The area of Jamaica is 10 800 km².
What is the population density of Jamaica?

Extending the Number System

What you need to know

- **Rational numbers** can be written in the form $\frac{a}{b}$, where a and b are integers ($b \neq 0$).

  Examples of rational numbers are: 2, -5, $\frac{2}{5}$, 0.6, 3.47, $1\frac{3}{4}$.

- All fractions can be written as decimals.

  For example, $\frac{1}{3} = 0.3333333\ldots = 0.\dot{3}$, $\frac{123}{999} = 0.123123123\ldots = 0.\dot{1}2\dot{3}$

- You should be able to convert a recurring decimal to a fraction.

  Eg 1 Find the fraction which is equal to $0.\dot{2}\dot{7}$, in its simplest form.

  $x = 0.2727\ldots$
  2 digits recur, so, multiply by 100.
  $100x = 27.2727\ldots$
  $99x = 27$
  $x = \frac{27}{99} = \frac{3}{11}$
  $0.\dot{2}\dot{7} = \frac{3}{11}$

  > Let $x =$ the recurring decimal.
  > Multiply both sides by a power of 10:
  > - by $10^1 = 10$ if only 1 digit recurs,
  > - by $10^2 = 100$ if 2 digits recur, and so on.
  >
  > Subtract the original equation from the new equation.
  > Solve the resulting equation for x.
  > If necessary, write the fraction in its simplest form.

- All **terminating** and **recurring decimals** are rational numbers.

- A **surd** is the root of a rational number which is not rational.
  A surd is an **irrational number**.

  These are examples of surds: $\sqrt{2}$ $\sqrt{0.37}$ $3 + \sqrt{2}$
  $\sqrt{9}$ is not a surd because $\sqrt{9} = 3$ which is rational.

  > $\sqrt{a}$ means the positive square root of a.

- Rules for manipulating and simplifying surds:

  $$\sqrt{ab} = \sqrt{a} \times \sqrt{b} \qquad m\sqrt{a} + n\sqrt{a} = (m + n)\sqrt{a} \qquad \sqrt{\frac{a}{b}} = \frac{\sqrt{a}}{\sqrt{b}}$$

  Eg 2 Simplify the following leaving the answers in surd form.

  (a) $\sqrt{32} = \sqrt{16} \times \sqrt{2} = 4\sqrt{2}$

  > Look for factors that are square numbers.

  (b) $\sqrt{8} + \sqrt{18} = \sqrt{4} \times \sqrt{2} + \sqrt{9} \times \sqrt{2} = 2\sqrt{2} + 3\sqrt{2} = 5\sqrt{2}$

  (c) $\sqrt{\frac{72}{20}} = \frac{\sqrt{72}}{\sqrt{20}} = \frac{\sqrt{36}\sqrt{2}}{\sqrt{4}\sqrt{5}} = \frac{6\sqrt{2}}{2\sqrt{5}} = \frac{3\sqrt{2}}{\sqrt{5}}$

- To **rationalise** the denominator of a fraction of the form $\frac{a}{\sqrt{b}}$ multiply both the numerator (top) and the denominator (bottom) of the fraction by $\sqrt{b}$.

  Eg 3 Rationalise the denominator and simplify where possible: $\frac{3\sqrt{2}}{6}$.

  $$\frac{3\sqrt{2}}{\sqrt{6}} = \frac{3\sqrt{2}}{\sqrt{6}} \times \frac{\sqrt{6}}{\sqrt{6}} = \frac{3\sqrt{2}\sqrt{6}}{6} = \frac{3\sqrt{2}\sqrt{2}\sqrt{3}}{6} = \frac{6\sqrt{3}}{6} = \sqrt{3}$$

- You should be able to use surds in calculations.

  > To keep an answer exact it is necessary to keep numbers like $\sqrt{3}$ in surd form.

1 (a) Change $\frac{5}{7}$ into a decimal.

(b) Find the fraction which is equal to $0.\dot{2}$. Give your answer in its simplest terms.

2 Simplify the following as much as possible.

(a) $\sqrt{2} \times \sqrt{8}$ (b) $\sqrt{5} \times \sqrt{5} \times \sqrt{5} \times \sqrt{5}$ OCR

3 Simplify. (a) $2\sqrt{5} + 3\sqrt{5}$ (b) $\sqrt{3} \times \sqrt{3}$ (c) $\sqrt{2} \times \sqrt{3} \times \sqrt{6}$ (d) $\sqrt{\frac{9}{16}}$

4 (a) Prove that $0.4\dot{5} = \frac{5}{11}$.

(b) Write the number $0.\dot{6}\dot{3}$ as a fraction in its simplest form.

5 Write the recurring decimal $0.\dot{3}\dot{6}$ in the form $\frac{a}{b}$, where a and b are integers.

6 (a) Express 12 as the product of its prime factors.

(b) $\sqrt{12}$ can be written in the form of $a\sqrt{b}$ where a and b are prime numbers. Calculate the values of a and b.

7 Express each of the following in the form $a\sqrt{b}$ where a and b are integers and b is as small as possible.

(a) $\sqrt{45}$ (b) $\sqrt{27} + \sqrt{12}$ OCR

8 Write $\sqrt{18}$ in the form of $a\sqrt{b}$ where a and b are prime numbers.

9 (a) Simplify the following. Write your answer in the form $a\sqrt{b}$ where a and b are integers and b is as small as possible.

(i) $\sqrt{500}$ (ii) $\sqrt{50}$ (iii) $\sqrt{50} \times \sqrt{60}$

(b) Simplify the following fractions so that there is no root in the denominator.

(i) $\frac{1}{\sqrt{5}}$ (ii) $\frac{12}{\sqrt{3}}$ OCR

10 Simplify, leaving your answers where appropriate in surd form.

(a) $5\sqrt{3} - \sqrt{3}$ (b) $\sqrt{3} \times 3\sqrt{3}$ (c) $\frac{\sqrt{27}}{3}$ (d) $\sqrt{12} \times \sqrt{75}$

11 Simplify the expression $\sqrt{24}(\sqrt{50} - \sqrt{8})$.

12 Express each of the following in its simplest form with a rational denominator.

(a) $\frac{6}{\sqrt{3}}$ (b) $\frac{15}{2\sqrt{5}}$

13 (a) Given that $\sqrt{75} = k\sqrt{3}$, find the value of k.

(b) Rationalise the denominator of $\frac{18}{\sqrt{3}}$ and simplify your answer.

14 (a) Evaluate $\sqrt{6} \times \sqrt{15} \times \sqrt{10}$.

(b) $(\sqrt{6} + \sqrt{15})^2 = a + b\sqrt{10}$. Find the values of a and b.   OCR

15 It is given that $p = 3 + \sqrt{5}$ and $q = 2 - 3\sqrt{5}$.
Simplify the following.
Give each answer in the form $a + b\sqrt{5}$, where a and b are integers.

(a) $p + q$ (b) p^2 (c) pq OCR

16 You are given that $a = \sqrt{5} + 3$ and $b = \sqrt{5} - 3$.

(a) $a + b = \sqrt{n}$. Find the value of n.

(b) Find the value of $\frac{a - b}{ab}$.

Number
Non-calculator Paper

Do not use a calculator for this exercise.

1 Use these numbers to answer the following questions.

$$3 \quad 7 \quad 11 \quad 15 \quad 19 \quad 23 \quad 27$$

(a) Which number in the list is a factor of another number in the list?

(b) Which number is a cube number?

(c) (i) Which numbers are not prime numbers? Give a reason for your answer.

(ii) The numbers are part of a sequence.
What is the next number in the sequence which is not a prime number?

2 (a) Work out. (i) $5 - 0.26$ (ii) 0.2×0.4 (iii) $24 \div 0.3$

(b) A turkey costs £3.60 per kilogram.
What is the cost of a turkey which weighs 6.5 kilograms?

3 (a) Write these fractions in order, smallest first: $\frac{1}{2}$ $\frac{2}{3}$ $\frac{3}{5}$ $\frac{5}{8}$ $\frac{3}{4}$

(b) Write down a fraction that lies halfway between $\frac{1}{5}$ and $\frac{1}{4}$.

(c) Work out (i) $\frac{1}{4} + \frac{2}{5}$, (ii) $\frac{2}{3} - \frac{1}{2}$, (iii) $\frac{4}{5} \times \frac{2}{3}$.

4 A teacher has £1500 to spend on new books.
He wants 52 novels costing £9.95 each, 96 poetry books costing £6.99 each and 32 books of modern plays costing £14.75 each. He thinks he has enough money to buy all these books.
Show a rough calculation to check whether he is right.   OCR

5 (a) Conrad cycles 24 km in $1\frac{1}{2}$ hours. What is his cycling speed in kilometres per hour?

(b) Cas cycles 24 km at 15 km/h. She sets off at 0930. At what time does she finish?

6 (a) Given that $46.2 \times 127 = 5867.4$, write down the value of:

(i) 462×1270, (ii) $\frac{58.674}{127}$.

(b) Estimate the value of $\frac{3062}{52 \times 19}$. Show all the approximations you make.   OCR

7 (a) Find. (i) the cube root of 64 (ii) the reciprocal of 0.1

(b) Work out. $1\frac{2}{3} + 2\frac{3}{4}$ OCR

8 (a) Work out $5^2 \times 2^3$.

(b) Write 30 as a product of prime factors.   OCR

9 (a) In a sale, raspberries are reduced from £5 to £4 per kg and blackberries reduced from £4.50 to £3.50 per kg.
Without doing any calculation, explain which is the greater proportional reduction.

(b) In a summer fruit pudding, raspberries and blackberries are used in the ratio 4 : 1.
A pudding contains a total of 150 g of raspberries and blackberries.
What weight of raspberries does the pudding contain?

(c) The raspberries were reduced from £5 to £4 per kg.
Calculate the percentage decrease in the cost of the raspberries.

(d) A tray of raspberries weighs 9 kg, correct to the nearest kg.
What is the least weight that the tray of raspberries could be?   OCR

10 A youth club organises a skiing holiday for 45 children. The ratio of boys to girls is 5 : 4.
40% of the boys have skied before. How many boys have skied before?

11 (a) Write as a product of its prime factors: (i) 48, (ii) 108.

(b) Hence, find the least common multiple of 48 and 108.

12 (a) Evaluate the following. (i) 9^0 (ii) 6^{-2} (iii) $64^{\frac{1}{2}}$

     (b) Write the following as a single power of 3. $\dfrac{3^5 \times 3^3}{(3^3)^2}$

     (c) Write 0.000 094 in standard form.

     (d) Write 3.82×10^5 as an ordinary number. OCR

13 Hugh buys a box of fireworks.
After lighting 40% of the fireworks he has 24 fireworks left.
How many fireworks did he buy?

14 Sally has a shelf which is 250 cm long, correct to the nearest centimetre.
She cuts off a piece which is 75 cm long, correct to the nearest centimetre.
What is the upper bound of the length of the remaining piece of shelf? OCR

15 Work out.   (a) $1\frac{1}{4} \times 2\frac{2}{3}$ (b) $2\frac{1}{2} \div 1\frac{2}{3}$

16 Two cucumbers and three lettuces cost £2.64.
A cucumber costs 25% more than a lettuce.
Find the cost of a cucumber.

17 Felix and Jan are in cars travelling in opposite directions along a motorway.
At 1015 they are 30 km apart and travelling towards each other.
Felix is travelling at an average speed of 70 km/h.
If they pass each other at 1027, what is Jan's average speed?

18 The ratio of male to female passengers on a bus is 3 : 5.
At the next stop 5 females get off and 2 males get on.
The ratio of male to female passengers is now 4 : 5.
How many male passengers are now on the bus?

19 (a) Evaluate $(6 \times 10^5) \times (5 \times 10^{-2})$, giving your answer in standard form.

     (b) (i) Write $\sqrt{8}$ in the form $a\sqrt{2}$.

           (ii) Simplify. $\sqrt{18} - \sqrt{8}$ OCR

20 (a) Write 240 as the product of its prime factors.

     (b) Hence, find the smallest whole number 240 must be multiplied by to give a perfect square.

21 It takes 15 minutes to fill a paddling pool at the rate of 12 litres per minute.
How long will it take to fill the pool at the rate of 20 litres per minute?

22 Evaluate.   (a) $\left(\sqrt{6}\right)^4$ (b) $49^{\frac{1}{2}} \times 7^{-2}$ (c) $\left(2 - \sqrt{5}\right)\left(2 + \sqrt{5}\right)$ OCR

23 (a) What is the reciprocal of 2.5?

     (b) Write these numbers in descending order.

$$5^{-1} \qquad \left(\tfrac{1}{4}\right)^{\frac{1}{2}} \qquad 2^{-3} \qquad 3^{-2} \qquad \left(\tfrac{1}{2}\right)^2$$

     (c) Find the value of x when:
        (i) $2^4 \times 2^3 = 2^x$,   (ii) $3^{-2} \div 3^{-4} = 3^x$,   (iii) $216^{\frac{1}{3}} = 6^x$.

24 A jug holds 4.6 litres of milk, correct to one decimal place.
Write down the lower and upper bounds of the amount of milk in the jug.

25 (a) (i) Simplify the following expression, leaving your answer in surd form. $\sqrt{27} + \sqrt{75}$

         (ii) **Hence**, simplify the expression $\dfrac{\sqrt{27} + \sqrt{75}}{\sqrt{12}}$.

     (b) Calculate $64^{\frac{2}{3}}$.

     (c) Calculate $27^{-\frac{1}{3}}$, giving your answer as a fraction.

     (d) Write the number $0.2\overset{..}{1}$ as a fraction in its simplest form.

Number
Calculator Paper

You may use a calculator for this exercise.

1 Jacob is 3.7 kg heavier than Isaac. The sum of their weights is 44.5 kg. How heavy is Jacob?

2 (a) Write the number 52.03718 correct to:
   (i) 3 decimal places   (ii) 2 decimal places   (iii) 1 decimal place
   (b) Use your calculator to work these out.
   (i) $\sqrt{44.89}$ (ii) 2.9^2 (iii) $11 + 4.5 \times 12$ (iv) $\dfrac{8}{10.3 - 7.9}$ OCR

3 To make 16 Viennese shortcakes you need:

200 g of flour	225 g of butter	80 g of icing sugar	50 g of cornflour	A little red jam

   (a) Mary made 40 Viennese shortcakes.
   How much icing sugar did she use?
   (b) Gretchen is going to make some Viennese shortcakes. She has 375 g of flour.
   How many can she make?
   (c) The ingredients for the 16-cake recipe cost £1.12 in total. The cakes are to be sold at a fete.
   How much should be charged for each cake to make 85% profit on the cost?
   Give your answer correct to the nearest penny.   OCR

4 560 people live in a village. Of these, 320 are adults and 240 are children.
   (a) Calculate, in its lowest terms, the ratio of adults to children.
   (b) The village stages a pantomime.
   Half of the adults and three quarters of the children go to see it.
   What percentage of the total population of the village see the pantomime?
   (c) A pantomime ticket costs £3.50 for an adult. The price is reduced by 40% for a child.
   Calculate the cost of a pantomime ticket for a child.   OCR

5 The diagram shows the weights and prices of two packets
   of gravy granules.
   This week both packets are on special offer.
   The smaller packet has one third off the normal price.
   The larger packet has 30% off the normal price.
   Which packet is better value this week? Show your working.

Gravy Granules
180 g
Normal price
54p

Gravy Granules
300 g
Normal price
90p

6 To make squash, orange juice and water is mixed in the ratio of 1 : 6.
   How much orange juice is needed to make 3.5 litres of squash?

7 A train took 3 hours 30 minutes to travel the 238 miles from London to Preston.
   Calculate, in miles per hour, the average speed of the train.   OCR

8 Ruby buys a new exhaust for her car. The cost is £98 plus $17\frac{1}{2}$% VAT.
   How much does she have to pay altogether?

9 (a) Use your calculator to work this out. $\dfrac{1}{2.5} + \dfrac{10}{0.625}$
   (b) Write 0.7, 11%, 0.08 and $\dfrac{9}{20}$ in ascending order of size.
   Show working to support your answer.
   (c) 1.2 kg of tomatoes and 0.3 kg of mushrooms cost a total of £1.95.
   Tomatoes cost £1.10 per kilogram.
   Find the cost of 1 kg of mushrooms.   OCR

10 Josie invests £800 in an account that pays her 3% simple interest every year.
   How much interest will she have been paid in total after 6 years?   OCR

11 A caravan is for sale at £7200. Stuart buys the caravan on credit.
The credit terms are:

> deposit 25% of sale price and 36 monthly payments of £175.

Express the extra amount paid for credit, compared with the cash price, as a percentage of the cash price.

12 (a) (i) Calculate $\dfrac{612 \times 29.6}{81.3 - 18.9}$, correct to 3 significant figures.

      (ii) Use approximations to show that your answer is about right.

   (b) What is the reciprocal of 0.25?

13 Rasheed, Kerry and Anthony each buy heating oil at the same price per litre.
Rasheed bought 650 litres of oil for £286.

   (a) Kerry bought 800 litres of oil. How much did she pay?

   (b) Anthony paid £506. How much oil did he buy?   OCR

14 Calculate   (a) $\dfrac{1}{0.72 + 0.88}$,   (b) $(4.5)^2 + (3.5)^3$.   OCR

15 (a) James and Anne bought a new car for £14 756. They shared the cost in the ratio 4 : 3.
How much did Anne pay?

   (b) The next year the price increased from £14 756 to £15 999.
Calculate the percentage increase.   OCR

16 Karina says,

   "For some numbers the square root of the number is larger than the number itself."

For what numbers is this true?

17 At 20 miles per hour a bus journey takes 40 minutes.
A taxi does the same journey at 25 miles per hour.
How many minutes does the taxi take?

18 Five players in a school rugby team enter the lift.
Each player weighs 75 kg, to the nearest kilogram.
Is it possible that this group exceeds the maximum load?
Support your reasoning with calculation.

⊘	**LIFT RULES**	⊘
	MAXIMUM LOAD: 377 kg	
	MAXIMUM NUMBER OF	
⊘	**PERSONS: 5**	⊘

      OCR

19 Place the following numbers in order, largest first: $\sqrt{6.9}$ 2.58 1.6^2 $2\frac{4}{7}$

20 In 2004, Ashley's council tax bill was £965.40.
In 2005, Ashley's council tax bill was 6.8% more than in 2004.
In 2006, Ashley's council tax bill was 4.9% more than in 2005.
Calculate the percentage increase in council tax between 2004 and 2006.

21 (a) (i) Write the reciprocal of $1\frac{1}{2}$ as a fraction.

      (ii) Write the reciprocal of 40 as a decimal.

   (b) Calculate the difference between 5^{-2} and 2^{-5}.
Give your answer in standard form.   OCR

22 In 2005, the population of the World was estimated to be 6700 million.
If the population increases at the rate of 1.7% per year, estimate the population of the World in 2010. Give your answer correct to 3 significant figures.

23 (a) Write 0.000765 in standard form.

   (b) Calculate. $\dfrac{(4.5 \times 10^{-3}) \times (5.8 \times 10^{6})}{2.7 \times 10^{-5}}$.

      Give your answer in standard form, correct to 2 significant figures.   OCR

24 $p = 3^2 \times 5 \times 7$ and $q = 2 \times 3 \times 5^2$. Find the least common multiple of p and q.

25 The population of China is 1.2×10^9. The area of China is 9.5×10^6 square kilometres. What is the population density of China?

26 (a) In 2005, the food production of a country was 7.275 million tonnes.
This was 3% less than in 2004.
Calculate the food production in 2004.

(b) Some of the food was transported overnight by sea. The ship sailed at 1850.
It travelled 408 km to its destination at an average speed of 28 km/h.
At what time did it arrive? OCR

27 (a) You are given the formula $k = \frac{3}{4} m^2$.
Calculate the exact value of k, when $m = 4.8 \times 10^3$.
Give your answer in standard form.

(b) Calculate $\sqrt{\dfrac{5.2 \times 10^{-3}}{(0.039)^2}}$, correct to two decimal places.

28 (a) Jools invests £2000 at 6.5% per annum compound interest.
Calculate the value of his investment at the end of 3 years.

(b) Jennifer gets 6% per annum on her investment.
After one year the value of her investment is £1272.
How much did she invest?

29 Last year Alf had a tax allowance of £4895 and paid £4697 in tax. The rates of tax were:

> 10p in the £ on the first £2090 of taxable income and
> 22p in the £ on all the remaining taxable income.

How much did Alf earn last year?

30 One day a shop sold 369 books.
This was an increase of 2.5% on the number of books sold the previous day.
How many books did the shop sell on the previous day? OCR

31 The land area of France is 5.41×10^5 square kilometres.
The land area of the Earth is 1.32×10^8 square kilometres.
Calculate the land area of France as a percentage of the land area of the Earth.
Give your answer to a suitable degree of accuracy.

32 (a) Write $\sqrt{45}$ in the form $a\sqrt{b}$ where a and b are prime numbers.

(b) Write $\dfrac{5}{\sqrt{10}}$ in the form $\dfrac{\sqrt{a}}{b}$ where a and b are whole numbers.

(c) Express $\sqrt{32}$ as a power of 2.

(d) Simplify $4^0 + 4^{-1} + 4^{-2}$.

(e) Write $0.2\ddot{7}$ as a fraction in its simplest form.

33 A sum of money invested on March 1st, 1995, has increased by 4.5% each year.
On March 1st, 2005, the investment was worth £13 200.24.
Calculate, to the nearest pound, how much was invested in 1995. OCR

34 Calculate the value of $(5.8 \times 10^{-5})^{\frac{1}{3}}$.
Give your answer in standard form correct to 2 significant figures.

35 (a) Simplify $\sqrt{3} \times (5 - 2\sqrt{3})^2$.
Give your answer in the form $p + q\sqrt{3}$, where p and q are integers.

(b) Write each of the following expressions in the form $k\sqrt{a}$, where k is an integer and a is 2, 3 or 5.
(i) $\sqrt{10} \times \sqrt{5}$ (ii) $\dfrac{\sqrt{160}}{\sqrt{20}}$ OCR

Introduction to Algebra

What you need to know

- You should be able to write **algebraic expressions**.

  Eg 1 An expression for the cost of 6 pens at n pence each is $6n$ pence.

  Eg 2 An expression for 2 pence more than n pence is $n + 2$ pence.

- Be able to **simplify expressions** by collecting **like terms** together.

  Eg 3 (a) $2d + 3d = 5d$ (b) $3x + 2 - x + 4 = 2x + 6$ (c) $x + 2x + x^2 = 3x + x^2$

- Be able to **multiply expressions** together.

  Eg 4 (a) $2a \times a = 2a^2$ (b) $y \times y \times y = y^3$ (c) $3m \times 2n = 6mn$

- Be able to recall and use these properties of powers:
  Powers of the same base are **added** when terms are **multiplied**.
  Powers of the same base are **subtracted** when terms are **divided**.
  Powers are **multiplied** when a power is raised to a power.

  $$a^m \times a^n = a^{m+n}$$
  $$a^m \div a^n = a^{m-n}$$
  $$(a^m)^n = a^{m \times n}$$

  Eg 5 (a) $x^3 \times x^2 = x^5$ (b) $a^5 \div a^2 = a^3$ (c) $6m^6 \div 2m^2 = 3m^4$ (d) $(2y^2)^3 = 8y^6$

- Be able to **multiply out brackets**.

  Eg 6 (a) $2(x - 5) = 2x - 10$ (b) $x(x - 5) = x^2 - 5x$ (c) $2m(m + 3) = 2m^2 + 6m$

- Be able to **factorise expressions**.

  Eg 7 (a) $3x - 6 = 3(x - 2)$ (b) $m^2 + 5m = m(m + 5)$ (c) $3a^2 - 6a = 3a(a - 2)$

Exercise 10

1 Godfrey is 5 years older than Mary.
Write expressions for the following
(a) Godfrey's age when Mary is t years old.
(b) Mary's age when Godfrey is x years old.

2 A cup of coffee costs x pence and a cup of tea costs y pence.
Write an expression for the cost of 3 cups of coffee and 2 cups of tea.

3 Simplify (a) $m + 2m + 3m$,   (b) $2m + 2 - m$,   (c) $m \times m \times m$.

4 Write an expression, in terms of x,
for the sum of the angles in this shape.

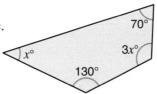

5 A muffin costs $d + 3$ pence.
Write an expression for the cost of 5 muffins.

6 Which of these algebraic expressions are equivalent?

$a + a$	$2(a + 1)$	$2a + 1$	$2a + 2$	a^3
a^2	$a + a + 1$	$2a$	$a + a + a$	$a \times a$

7 (a) Simplify (i) $2x + 3 + x$, (ii) $2x + y - x + y$.

(b) Multiply out (i) $2(x + 3)$, (ii) $x(x - 1)$.

(c) Multiply out and simplify (i) $2(x - 1) - 3$, (ii) $7 + 3(2 + x)$.

(d) Factorise (i) $2a - 6$, (ii) $x^2 + 2x$.

8 (a) Simplify. $3p + 5t + 7 - 2p + t + 9$

(b) Multiply out the brackets. $2(3p - 5t)$

OCR

9 (a) Simplify $2ab + 3a - 2b + b - 5a + ab$.

(b) Multiply out and simplify $3(2x + 3) + 2(5 + x)$.

10 Bananas cost x pence each.

I buy 6 bananas and pay with a £5 note.

Write down, in terms of x, how much change I will get.

Give your answer in pence.

OCR

11 Lorna buys some 1st class stamps and some 2nd class stamps.

She buys 12 stamps altogether.

(a) She buys x 1st class stamps.

Write an expression for the number of 2nd class stamps she buys.

(b) 2nd class stamps cost d pence.

A 1st class stamp costs 5 pence more than a 2nd class stamp.

Write an expression for the cost of a 1st class stamp.

(c) Write an expression, in terms of x and d, for the amount Lorna has to pay for her 12 stamps. Give your answer in its simplest form.

12 Simplify. (a) $y^3 \times y^2$ (b) $x^6 \div x^3$ (c) $\dfrac{z^4 \times z}{z^3}$ (d) $\dfrac{x^2 y}{xy^2}$

13 Factorise completely. $15x^2 + 9xy$

OCR

14 (a) Simplify $5 - 3(2n - 1)$.

(b) Multiply out $(-3m) \times (-2m)$.

(c) Factorise fully $8mn - 2m$.

15 Expand and simplify $3(2x + 3) - 2(5 + x)$.

16 (a) Simplify (i) $2a^3 \times 3a$, (ii) $6x^8 \div 3x^2$, (iii) $\dfrac{3m^2 \times 4n^6}{6mn^2}$, (iv) $4x^3 y \times 5x^2 y$.

(b) Expand (i) $(3m^3)^2$, (ii) $(2a^2 b)^3$.

17 (a) Expand the brackets. (i) $2x(x - 3y)$ (ii) $3a(3a + a^2)$

(b) Factorise. (i) $4xy - 2y^2$ (ii) $3m^2 - 12m$

(c) Simplify. $2x^2 - x(1 + x)$

18 (a) Multiply out the brackets and simplify where possible.

(i) $3(2x + 5) - 2(x - 1)$ (ii) $x(3x^2 + 5)$

(b) Simplify the following.

(i) $a^5 \times a^2$ (ii) $(2x^2 y)^3$ (iii) $\dfrac{(2x^2 y)^3}{x^3 y^{-2}}$

OCR

19 (a) Multiply out $2x(2y - xy)$.

(b) Factorise $6pq - 3pq^2$.

(c) Simplify $21m^6 \div 7m^3$.

20 Simplify. (a) $\dfrac{6x^2 z \times 2x^2 y^2 z}{3x^3 y}$ (b) $\sqrt{\dfrac{1}{m^6}}$

21 Simplify fully $\dfrac{3a^2}{bc} \times \dfrac{b^2}{6ac^2} \times \dfrac{2ac^2}{b}$.

Solving Equations

What you need to know

- The solution of an equation is the value of the unknown letter that fits the equation.

- You should be able to solve simple equations by **inspection**.

- Be able to solve simple problems by **working backwards**.

  Eg 1 I think of a number, multiply it by 3 and add 4. The answer is 19.

  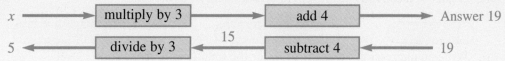

  The number I thought of is 5.

- Be able to use the **balance method** to solve equations.

  Eg 2 Solve these equations.

  (a) $d - 13 = -5$ (b) $-4a = 20$ (c) $5 - 4n = -1$

  $d = -5 + 13$ $a = \frac{20}{-4}$ $-4n = -6$

  $d = 8$ $a = -5$ $n = 1.5$

- Be able to solve equations with unknowns on both sides of the equals sign.

  Eg 3 Solve $3x + 1 = x + 7$.

  $3x = x + 6$

  $2x = 6$

  $x = 3$

- Be able to solve equations which include brackets.

  Eg 4 Solve $4(3 + 2x) = 5(x + 2)$.

  $12 + 8x = 5x + 10$

  $8x = 5x - 2$

  $3x = -2$

  $x = -\frac{2}{3}$

- Be able to solve equations which involve fractions.

  Eg 5 Solve $\frac{x}{2} + \frac{2x}{3} = 7$.

  $6 \times \frac{x}{2} + 6 \times \frac{2x}{3} = 6 \times 7$

  $3x + 4x = 42$

  $7x = 42$

  $x = 6$

  Eg 6 Solve $\frac{x - 1}{3} = \frac{x + 1}{4}$.

  $4(x - 1) = 3(x + 1)$

  $4x - 4 = 3x + 3$

  $4x = 3x + 7$

  $x = 7$

- You should be able to write, or form, equations using the information given in a problem.

Exercise 11

1 Solve these equations.   (a) $7 + x = 12$ (b) $5 - x = 3$ (c) $5x - 9 = 11$

2 (a) I think of a number, add 3, and then multiply by 2. The answer is 16.
       What is my number?

   (b) I think of a number, double it and then subtract 3. The answer is 5.
       What is my number?

3 Solve these equations.

   (a) $3x - 7 = 23$ (b) $5 + 7x = 47$ (c) $5(x - 2) = 20$ (d) $3x - 7 = x + 15$

4 Solve these equations. (a) $\frac{x}{2} = 2$ (b) $4x + 3 = 27$ (c) $8x - 3 = 6x + 15$ OCR

5 Solve these equations.
(a) $7x + 4 = 60$ (b) $3x - 7 = -4$ (c) $2(x + 3) = -2$ (d) $3x - 4 = 1 + x$

6 Solve. (a) $5x + 4 = 2x + 8$ (b) $3(x + 10) = 24$ OCR

7 Solve these equations.
(a) $2x + 5 = 2$ (b) $2(x - 1) = 3$ (c) $5 - 2x = 3x + 2$ (d) $2(3 + x) = 9$

8 (a) Multiply out and simplify. $3(x + 4) - 8x$
(b) Solve. $6x - 5 = 15 - 2x$ OCR

9 The lengths of these rods are given, in centimetres, in terms of n.

n $n + 3$ $2n - 1$

(a) Write an expression, in terms of n, for the total length of the rods.
(b) The total length of the rods is 30 cm.
By forming an equation, find the value of n.

10 Ice lollies cost x pence each.
Ice creams cost 90 pence each.
The total cost of three ice lollies and one ice cream is £2.85.
(a) Write down an equation in x.
(b) Solve your equation to find the cost of one ice lolly. OCR

11 Solve the equation $4(3 - x) = 20$.

12 Solve these equations. (a) $3x - 5 = 16$ (b) $7x + 1 = 2x + 4$

13 Solve the equation $5(x - 3) = 2x$.

14 A cracker costs n pence.
A party hat costs 7 pence less than a cracker.
(a) Write an expression for the cost of a party hat.
(b) The cost of 10 crackers and 5 party hats is £4.45
By forming an equation in n find the cost of a party hat.

15 (a) Expand. $x(x - 3)$
(b) Solve. $8y + 13 = 3(y + 1)$ OCR

16 Solve these equations.
(a) $2(x - 3) + 3(x + 1) = 2$
(b) $3(2 + 3a) = 5(a - 2)$
(c) $x - 3(x + 1) = 2(5 - 2x)$

17 Solve these equations. (a) $5(x + 7) = 3x + 29$ (b) $\frac{8y + 16}{3} = y - 8$ OCR

18 Solve the equations (a) $\frac{x - 3}{4} = 1 - x$, (b) $\frac{x - 3}{2} = \frac{2x + 1}{3}$.

19 Solve the equation $\frac{1}{2}(x - 3) = \frac{1}{4}(3x - 1)$.

20 Solve the equation $\frac{x - 1}{3} + \frac{x + 1}{2} = \frac{5}{6}$.

21 Solve the equation $\frac{2(x + 1)}{3} - \frac{x + 2}{5} = 4$.

Formulae ●●●●●●●●●●●●●●●

What you need to know

- An **expression** is just an answer using letters and numbers.
  A **formula** is an algebraic rule. It always has an equals sign.

- You should be able to **write simple formulae**.

  Eg 1 A packet of crisps weighs 25 grams.
  Write a formula for the total weight,
  W grams, of n packets of crisps.
  $$W = 25n$$

  Eg 2 Start with t, add 5 and then multiply
  by 3. The result is p.
  Write a formula for p in terms of t.
  $$p = 3(t + 5)$$

- Be able to **substitute** values into expressions and formulae.

  Eg 3 (a) $A = pq - r$
  Find the value of A
  when $p = 2$,
  $q = -2$ and $r = 3$.
  $A = pq - r$
  $A = 2 \times (-2) - 3$
  $A = -4 - 3$
  $A = -7$

  (b) $M = 2n^2$
  Find the value of M
  when $n = 3$.
  $M = 2n^2$
  $M = 2 \times 3^2$
  $M = 2 \times 9$
  $M = 18$

  (c) Find the value of $\dfrac{b^2c}{d}$
  when $b = \frac{1}{2}$, $c = 4.8$
  and $d = -3$.
  $\dfrac{b^2c}{d} = \dfrac{\left(\frac{1}{2}\right)^2 \times 4.8}{-3}$
  $\dfrac{b^2c}{d} = \dfrac{\frac{1}{4} \times 4.8}{-3}$
  $\dfrac{b^2c}{d} = \dfrac{1.2}{-3}$
  $\dfrac{b^2c}{d} = 0.4$

- Be able to **rearrange** a formula to make another letter (variable) the subject.

  Eg 4 $y = 2x + a$

  Make x the subject of the formula.
  $y = 2x + a$
  $y - a = 2x$
  $\dfrac{y - a}{2} = x$
  So, $x = \dfrac{y - a}{2}$

  Eg 5 $T = ab^2$
  Rearrange the formula to give b
  in terms of T and a.
  $T = ab^2$
  $\dfrac{T}{a} = b^2$
  $b = \pm \sqrt{\dfrac{T}{a}}$

Exercise 12

Do not use a calculator for questions 1 to 12.

1 Given that $m = -3$ and $n = 5$, find the value of
(a) $m + n$,   (b) $m - n$,   (c) $n - m$,   (d) mn.

2 (a) Find the value of $3n - 1$ when the value of n is: (i) 57,   (ii) -5,
(iii) Is the value of $3n - 1$ always an even number? Explain your answer.
(b) $P = 3a + 2b$. Find the value of b when $P = 27$ and $a = 5$.   OCR

3 $L = 5(p + q)$. Find the value of L when $p = 2$ and $q = -4$.

4 $A = b - cd$. Find the value of A when $b = -3$, $c = 2$ and $d = 4$.

5 For the formula $F = a^2 - 3b$, find the value of F when
(a) $a = 5$, $b = 2$,   (b) $a = -4$, $b = -2$.   OCR

6 What is the value of $10y^2$ when $y = 3$?

7 Work out the value of $2x^2$ when (a) $x = 3$, (b) $x = -4$. OCR

8 What is the value of $3x^3$ when $x = 2$?

9 $T = \frac{uv}{w}$. Find the value of T when $u = 3$, $v = -2$ and $w = \frac{1}{2}$.

10 $M = \sqrt{\frac{a}{b}}$. Find the value of M when $a = 8$ and $b = \frac{1}{2}$.

11 Eve buys n pints of milk at 35 pence a pint.
She pays for them with a £2 coin. She is given C pence change.
Write down a formula for C in terms of n.

12 This rule is used to change miles into kilometres.

> Multiply the number of miles by 8 and then divide by 5

(a) Use the rule to change 25 miles into kilometres.
(b) Using K for the number of kilometres and M for the number of miles write a formula for K in terms of M.
(c) Use your formula to find the value of M when $K = 60$.

13 (a) $A = x^2 + 3x$. Find the value of A when $x = -5$.
(b) Rearrange this formula to make n the subject. $C = 10n - 5$ OCR

14 Rearrange the formula $n = 3 + mp$ to make m the subject.

15 Rearrange the equation $3p + 2q = 5$ to make q the subject. OCR

16 $m = 3(n - 17)$. Find the value of n when $m = -9$.

17 Rearrange the formula $C = \frac{3r}{4}$ to make r the subject. OCR

18 You are given the formula $v = u + at$.
(a) Find v when $u = 17$, $a = -8$ and $t = \frac{3}{5}$.
(b) Rearrange the formula to give a in terms of v, u and t.

19 Make r the subject of the formula $p = \frac{gr}{s}$.

20 Rearrange the formula $T = 2\pi\sqrt{\frac{L}{G}}$ to make L the subject. OCR

21 You are given the formula $g = \frac{3}{5}h^2$.
(a) Find the value of g when $h = 2.5 \times 10^3$.
(b) Rearrange the formula to give h in terms of g.

22 The formula for the surface area, A, of a closed box is given by
$A = 2wb + 2wh + 2bh$. Rearrange this formula to make b the subject.

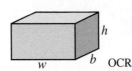

OCR

23 Rearrange the formula $p = \frac{q}{5 - q}$ to make q the subject.

24 Rearrange each of the following to give d in terms of e.
(a) $e = 5d + 3$ (b) $\frac{3d - 7}{4 + 5d} = e$ OCR

25 Make v the subject of the formula $w = \frac{uv}{u + v}$.

26 $n = \frac{3 + m}{m - 5}$. Rearrange the formula to give m in terms of n.

Sequences ●●●●●●●●●●●●●

What you need to know

- A **sequence** is a list of numbers made according to some rule.
  The numbers in a sequence are called **terms**.

- You should be able to draw and continue number sequences represented by patterns of shapes.

- Be able to continue a sequence by following a given rule.

  Eg 1 The sequence 2, 7, 22, … is made using the rule:

  > Multiply the last number by 3, then add 1.

  The next term in the sequence = $(22 \times 3) + 1 = 66 + 1 = 67$

- Be able to find a rule, and then use it, to continue a sequence.

  > **To continue a sequence:**
  > 1. Work out the rule to get from one term to the next.
  > 2. Apply the same rule to find further terms in the sequence.

  Eg 2 Describe the rule used to make the following sequences.
  Then use the rule to find the next term of each sequence.
  - (a) 5, 8, 11, 14, …   Rule: add 3 to last term.   Next term: 17.
  - (b) 2, 4, 8, 16, …   Rule: multiply last term by 2.   Next term: 32.
  - (c) 1, 1, 2, 3, 5, 8, …   Rule: add the last two terms.   Next term: 13.

- Special sequences   **Square numbers:**   1, 4, 9, 16, 25, …
                        Triangular numbers: 1, 3, 6, 10, 15, …

- A number sequence which increases (or decreases) by the same amount from one term to the next is called a **linear sequence**.
  The sequence: 2, 8, 14, 20, 26, … has a **common difference** of 6.

- You should be able to find an expression for the nth term of a linear sequence.

  Eg 3 Find the nth term of the sequence: 3, 5, 7, 9, …
  The sequence is linear, common difference = 2.
  To find the nth term add one to the multiples of 2.
  So, the nth term is $2n + 1$.

- Be able to find an expression for the nth term of a **quadratic sequence**.

  Eg 4 Find the nth term of the sequence: 4, 7, 12, 19, …
  The sequence is not linear, because the differences between terms is increasing.
  Compare the sequence with the sequence of square numbers: 1, 4, 9, 16, …
  To find the nth term add 3 to the square numbers.
  So, the nth term is $n^2 + 3$.

Exercise **13**

1   What is the next number in each of these sequences?
- (a) 1, 2, 5, 10, …
- (b) 1, 3, 9, 27, …
- (c) 1, $\frac{1}{2}$, $\frac{1}{4}$, $\frac{1}{8}$, …

2 The first six terms of a sequence are shown. 1, 4, 5, 9, 14, 23, ...
Write down the next two terms.

3 Look at this sequence of numbers. 2, 5, 8, 11, ...
(a) What is the next number in the sequence?
(b) Is 30 a number in this sequence? Give a reason for your answer.

4 A sequence begins: 5, 15, 45, 135, ...
(a) Write down the rule, in words, used to get from one term to the next in the sequence.
(b) Use your rule to find the next term in the sequence.

5 (a) Here is the rule for a sequence.

> Multiply the previous term by 3 and subtract 2.

The first term of this sequence is 4.
Write down the next two terms of this sequence.
(b) Here are the first four terms of another sequence. 128, 64, 32, 16
   (i) Find the seventh term.
   (ii) Explain how you worked out your answer.
(c) Here is the rule for another sequence.

> Subtract 4 from the previous term.

The fourth term of this sequence is 34.
Find the first term.   OCR

6 The first three patterns in a sequence are shown.

Pattern 1   Pattern 2   Pattern 3

(a) How many squares are in pattern 20? Explain how you found your answer.
(b) Write an expression for the number of squares in the nth pattern.

7 (a) Write down the next two terms of this sequence. 18, 17, 15, 12, 8
(b) The nth term of another sequence is: $15 - 3n$.
Find the 5th term of this sequence.
(c) These are the first five terms of another sequence. 5, 9, 13, 17, 21
Find the nth term of this sequence.   OCR

8 Find the nth term of the following sequences.
(a) 5, 7, 9, 11, ...   (b) 1, 6, 11, 16, ...

9 (a) Here are the first four terms of a sequence. 200, 136, 104, 88
Explain how to work out the next two terms.
(b) Here are the first four terms of another sequence. -1, 1, 3, 5
Find the nth term of this sequence.
(c) The nth term, T, of another sequence is given by the formula $T = n^2 - 4$.
Write down the first three terms of this sequence.   OCR

10 Write down a formula for the nth term of each of these sequences.
(a) 3, 7, 11, 15, ...   (b) $\frac{1}{3}$, $\frac{2}{7}$, $\frac{3}{11}$, $\frac{4}{15}$, ...   OCR

11 A sequence begins: 3, 6, 11, 18, 27, ...
(a) Find the next two terms in this sequence.
(b) Explain why this is not a linear sequence.
(c) Explain how you can find the 20th term in the sequence without writing down all the previous terms.

12 Give the nth term of the following sequences.
(a) 1, 4, 9, 16, 25, 36, ...   (b) 4, 7, 12, 19, 28, 39, ...

Straight Line Graphs

What you need to know

- **Coordinates** are used to describe the position of a point on a graph.

- The x axis is the line $y = 0$.
  The y axis is the line $x = 0$.

- The graph of a linear function is a straight line.

- You should be able to draw the graph of a straight line.

  Eg 1 Draw the graph of $y = x + 1$ for values of x from -2 to 2.

  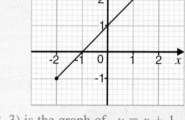

  > To draw a linear graph:
  > Find two corresponding values of x and y.
  > Plot the points.
  > Join the points with a straight line.

  When $x = -2$, $y = -2 + 1 = -1$. Plot $(-2, -1)$.
  When $x = 2$, $y = 2 + 1 = 3$. Plot $(2, 3)$.
  A straight line drawn through the points $(-2, -1)$ and $(2, 3)$ is the graph of $y = x + 1$.

- The equation of the graph of a straight line is of the form $y = mx + c$,
  where m is the gradient and c is the y-intercept.

  The **gradient** of a line can be found by drawing a
  right-angled triangle.

  $$\text{Gradient} = \frac{\text{distance up}}{\text{distance along}}$$

  Gradients can be positive, zero or negative.

  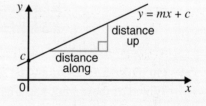

  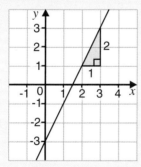

  Eg 2

  Find the equation of the line shown on this graph.

  $$\text{Gradient of line} = \frac{\text{distance up}}{\text{distance along}} = \frac{2}{1} = 2$$

  The graph crosses the y axis at the point $(0, -3)$,
  so, the y-intercept is -3.
  The equation of the line is $y = 2x - 3$.

- The points where a line crosses the axes can be found:
    by reading the coordinates from a graph,
    by substituting $x = 0$ and $y = 0$ into the equation of the line.

  Eg 3 The diagram shows a sketch of the line $2y = x + 3$.

  Find the coordinates of the points P and Q.

  When $x = 0$, $2y = 0 + 3$, $2y = 3$, $y = 1\frac{1}{2}$.

  When $y = 0$, $0 = x + 3$, $x = -3$.

  The points are $P\left(0, 1\frac{1}{2}\right)$ and $Q(-3, 0)$.

  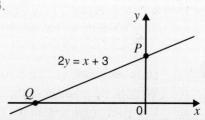

- You should be able to find the gradient of a line which is perpendicular to a given line.

If two lines are perpendicular to each other, the product of their gradients $= -1$.

This can be written as: $m_{AB} \times m_{CD} = -1$

where m_{AB} is the gradient of the line AB,
and m_{CD} is the gradient of the line CD.

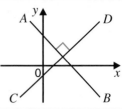

$$m_{AB} = \frac{-1}{m_{CD}}$$

Eg 4 Write down the gradient of the line which is perpendicular to the line with equation $y = -3x + 4$.
The gradient of the line $y = -3x + 4$ is -3.
The gradient of the line which is perpendicular to this line is $-1 \div (-3) = \frac{1}{3}$.

- Equations of the form $px + qy = r$ can be **rearranged** to the form $y = mx + c$.

Eg 5 The graph of a straight line is given by the equation $4y - 3x = 8$.
Write this equation in the form $y = mx + c$.

$4y - 3x = 8$
$4y = 3x + 8$
$y = \frac{3}{4}x + 2$

The line has gradient $\frac{3}{4}$ and y-intercept 2.

- You should be able to solve equations and problems involving straight line graphs.

Exercise 14

1 (a) Complete the table below for $y = 2x - 4$.

x	0	1	2	3	4	5
y	-4		0	2		6

(b) Draw the graph of $y = 2x - 4$.

OCR

2 (a) On the same axes, draw the graphs of $y = -2$, $y = x$ and $x + y = 5$.
(b) Which of these lines has a negative gradient?

3 Draw the graph of $y = 3x - 2$. Use values of x from 0 to 5.

OCR

4 (a) Draw the graph of $y = 1 - 2x$ for values of x from -3 to 3.
(b) Use your graph to find the value of y when $x = -1.5$.

5

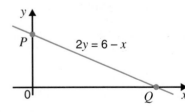

The diagram shows a sketch of the line $2y = 6 - x$.
(a) Find the coordinates of the points P and Q.
(b) The line $2y = 6 - x$ goes through $R(-5, m)$.
What is the value of m?

6 Points P, Q and R are shown on the grid.
(a) Write down the equation of the line PQ.
(b) (i) Use the grid to work out the gradient of the line RP.
(ii) Write down the equation of the line RP.

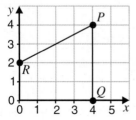

7 (a) Draw the graph of $2y = 3x - 6$ for values of x from -2 to 4.
(b) What is the gradient of the line $2y = 3x - 6$?
(c) Use your graph to find the value of x when $y = 1.5$.

8 Match these equations to their graphs.

1 $y = 2x$

2 $y - x = 2$

3 $y + x = 2$

4 $2y = x$

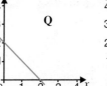

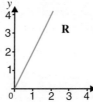

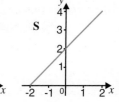

9 (a) (i) Work out the gradient of straight line L.
(ii) Write down the equation of line L.

(b) The equation of another line is $y = 2x - 3$.
Is this line parallel to line L?
Explain your answer.

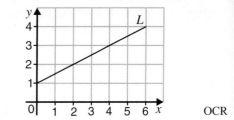

OCR

10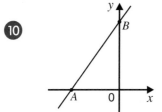

The diagram shows a sketch of the line passing through the points $A(-3, 0)$ and $B(0, 6)$.
(a) Find the gradient of the line AB.
(b) Find the equation of the line AB.

OCR

11 The graph shows the results of a science experiment.
A line of best fit has been put onto the graph.
Find the equation of the line.

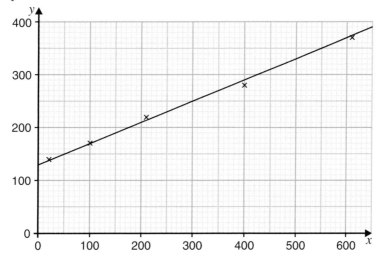

OCR

12 The equation of a line is $5y - 2x = 10$.

(a) Write this equation in the form $y = mx + c$.

(b) Write down the equation of the line, parallel to $5y - 2x = 10$, which passes through the point $(0, -1)$.

13 Show that the lines $5y = x + 4$ and $y = 6 - 5x$ are perpendicular to each other.

14 The diagram shows the graph of $2y = x + 4$.

Find the equation of the line through B which is perpendicular to the line $2y = x + 4$.

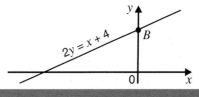

What you need to know

● A **gradient** measures the **rate of change** of one quantity with respect to another.
  A **positive** gradient represents a **rate of increase**.
  A **negative** gradient represents a **rate of decrease**.

● The gradient of a **distance-time graph** gives the speed.

> **Speed** is the rate of change of distance with respect to time.
> When the distance-time graph is **linear** the **speed is constant**.
> When the distance-time graph is **horizontal** the **speed is zero**.

Eg 1 The graph shows a car journey.
  (a) Between what times does the car travel fastest?
      Explain your answer.
  (b) What is the speed of the car during this part
      of the journey?

  (a) 1200 to 1230. Steepest gradient.
  (b) Speed $= \dfrac{\text{Distance}}{\text{Time}} = \dfrac{20\,\text{km}}{\frac{1}{2}\,\text{hour}} = 40\,\text{km/h}$

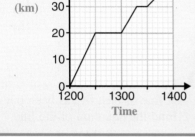

● The gradient of a **speed-time graph** gives the acceleration.

> **Acceleration** is the rate of change of speed with respect to time.
> When the speed-time graph is **linear** the **acceleration is constant**.
> When the speed-time graph is **horizontal** the **speed is constant** and the **acceleration is zero**.

● The **area** enclosed by the graph on a speed-time graph represents the **distance** travelled.

Eg 2 The graph shows the speed of a car against time between two roundabouts.
  (a) Calculate the acceleration of the car.
  (b) Calculate the distance travelled.

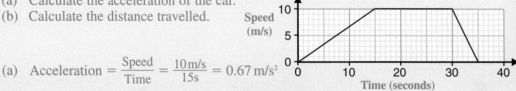

  (a) Acceleration $= \dfrac{\text{Speed}}{\text{Time}} = \dfrac{10\,\text{m/s}}{15\,\text{s}} = 0.67\,\text{m/s}^2$
  (b) Distance travelled $= \frac{1}{2}(15 + 35) \times 10 = 250$ metres

● You should be able to draw and interpret graphs which represent real-life situations.

Exercise 15

1 Water is poured into some containers at a constant rate.
   Copy the axes given and sketch the graph of the depth of the water against time for each
   container as it is filled.

   (a)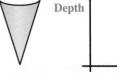

   (b)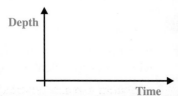

2 The graph shows Ahmed's journey.
He went to the post box then on to the minimarket.

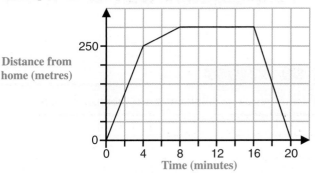

(a) The post box is 250 m from Ahmed's home.
How long did it take Ahmed to walk to the post box?
(b) How far is the minimarket from Ahmed's home?
(c) The last section of the graph slopes down.
What does this show?

OCR

3 Hassan is driving along a motorway.
The distance-time graph shows part of his journey.

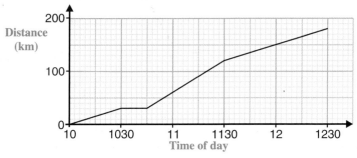

(a) Between which times is Hassan driving fastest?
(b) Calculate Hassan's speed between 10 am and 10.30 am.

OCR

4 Steve travelled from home to school by walking to a bus stop and then catching a school bus.
(a) Use the information below to construct a travel graph showing Steve's journey.
Steve left home at 0800.
He walked at 6 km/h for 10 minutes.
He then waited for 5 minutes before catching the bus.
The bus took him a further 8 km to school at a steady speed of 32 km/h.
(b) How far is Steve from home at 0820?
(c) (i) How long would it take Steve to cycle from home to school at an average speed of 15 km/h?
Give your answer in minutes.
(ii) Steve cycles at 15 km/h and wants to arrive at the same time as the bus in part (a).
At what time must he leave home?

OCR

5 The speed-time graph of a vehicle at the start of a journey is shown.

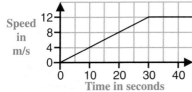

Calculate the acceleration of the vehicle in the first 20 seconds.

Inequalities ●●●●●●●●●●●●●

What you need to know

● **Inequalities** can be described using words or numbers and symbols.

Sign	Meaning
<	is less than
≤	is less than or equal to

Sign	Meaning
>	is greater than
≥	is greater than or equal to

● Inequalities can be shown on a **number line**.

Eg 1 This diagram shows the inequality: $-2 < x \leq 3$

```
    ○─────────────●
 -3  -2  -1   0   1   2   3   4
```

> The circle is: **filled** if the inequality is **included** (i.e. ≤ or ≥),
>   **not filled** if the inequality is **not included** (i.e. < or >).

● **Solving inequalities** means finding the values of x which make the inequality true.

> The same rules for equations can be applied to inequalities, with one exception:
> When you **multiply** (or **divide**) both sides of an inequality by a negative number
> the inequality is reversed. For example, if $-3x < 6$ then $x > -2$.

Eg 2 Solve these inequalities.

(a) $7a \geq a + 9$ (b) $-3x < 6$
     $6a \geq 9$ $x > -2$
     $a \geq 1.5$

> Divide both sides by -3.
> Because we are dividing by a negative number the inequality is reversed.

Eg 3 Find the integer values of n for which $-1 \leq 2n + 3 < 7$.

$$-1 \leq 2n + 3 < 7$$
$$-4 \leq 2n < 4$$
$$-2 \leq n < 2$$

Integer values which satisfy the inequality $-1 \leq 2n + 3 < 7$ are: $-2, -1, 0, 1$

● Inequalities can be shown on a graph. A line divides the graph into two **regions**.

> **To show an inequality on a graph:** Replace the inequality by '$=$' and draw the line.
> For > and < the line is **broken**. For ≥ and ≤ the line is **solid**.
> Test a point on each side of the line to see whether its coordinates satisfy the inequality.
> Label the required region.

Eg 4 Show the region which satisfies these inequalities:

$y < 3$, $1 < x < 4$ and $2y > x$.

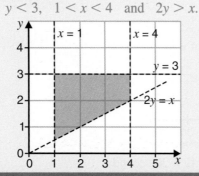

Eg 5 Use inequalities to describe the shaded region in this diagram.

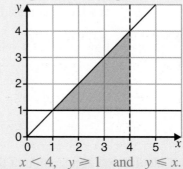

$x < 4$, $y \geq 1$ and $y \leq x$.

1 Solve these inequalities.
(a) $5x > 15$ (b) $x + 3 \geqslant 1$ (c) $x - 5 \leqslant 1$ (d) $3 + 2x > 7$

2 Draw number lines to show each of these inequalities.
(a) $x \geqslant -2$ (b) $\frac{x}{3} < -1$ (c) $-1 < x \leqslant 3$ (d) $x \leqslant -1$ **and** $x > 3$

3 (a) Solve. $2x - 1 \geqslant 5$
(b) Represent your solution to part (a) on a number line. OCR

4 Solve these inequalities.
(a) $2x \leqslant 6 - x$ (b) $3x > x + 7$ (c) $5x < 2x - 4$

5 List the values of n, where n is an integer such that:
(a) $-2 \leqslant 2n < 6$ (b) $-3 < n - 3 \leqslant -1$ (c) $-5 \leqslant 2n - 3 < 1$

6 Find all the integer values of n which satisfy $-15 < 5n \leqslant 20$. OCR

7 (a) Solve the inequality $3x - 5 \leqslant 1$.
(b) Write down the inequality shown by the following diagram.

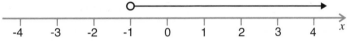

(c) Write down all the integers that satisfy both inequalities shown in parts (a) and (b).

8 Match each of the inequalities to its **unshaded** region.

1 $x + y < 2$
2 $y > 2$
3 $y > x$
4 $x < 2$

 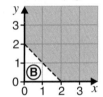 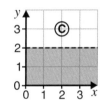 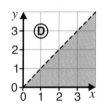

9 Draw and label axes for both x and y from 0 to 4.
(a) On your diagram draw and label the lines $y = 1$ and $x + y = 3$.
(b) Show clearly on the diagram the single region that is satisfied by all of these inequalities.
$x \geqslant 0$, $y \geqslant 1$, $x + y \leqslant 3$. Label this region R.

10 Write down three inequalities which describe the shaded region.

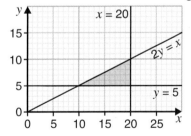

11 Solve this inequality. $4x + 9 > 12 - x$ OCR

12 (a) Solve the inequality $-4 \leqslant 2(x + 3) < 8$.
(b) n is an integer.
Find the maximum value of n that satisfies the inequality $-4 \leqslant 2(x + 3) < 8$.

13 (a) Solve each of the following inequalities. (i) $2x - 7 \leqslant 8 - x$ (ii) $3(2x + 1) > 15$
(b) Write down the whole number values of x which satisfy both of the above inequalities simultaneously.

What you need to know

- The graph of a **quadratic function** is a smooth curve and is called a **parabola**.

- The general equation of a **quadratic function** is $y = ax^2 + bx + c$, where a cannot be zero.
  The graph of a quadratic function is symmetrical and has a **maximum** or **minimum** value.

- You should be able to plot graphs of quadratic functions and use the graphs of quadratic functions to solve **quadratic equations**.

  Eg 1 (a) Draw the graph of $y = x^2 - x - 1$ for $-2 \leqslant x \leqslant 2$.
  (b) Hence, find the solutions of $x^2 - x - 1 = 0$.

  (a)

To draw a quadratic graph:
Make a table of values connecting x and y.
Plot the points.
Join the points with a smooth curve.

x	-2	-1	0	1	2
y	5	1	-1	-1	1

  (b) To solve $x^2 - x - 1 = 0$, read the values of x where the graph of $y = x^2 - x - 1$ crosses the x axis ($y = 0$).

  $x = -0.6$ and $x = 1.6$, correct to 1 d.p.

- Be able to use graphs of linear and quadratic functions to solve equations.

  Eg 2 You are given the graph of $y = 2x - x^2$.
  By drawing a suitable linear graph, on the same axes, find the solutions of $x^2 - 3x + 1 = 0$.
  To find the linear graph:
  Rearrange $x^2 - 3x + 1 = 0$ to give $1 - x = 2x - x^2$.
  Hence, the linear graph is $y = 1 - x$.
  Draw the graph of $y = 1 - x$ on the same diagram.

  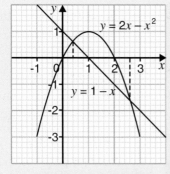

To solve $x^2 - 3x + 1 = 0$, read the values of x where the two graphs intersect.

  So, $x = 0.4$ and $x = 2.6$, correct to 1 d.p.

- The general form of a **cubic function** is $y = ax^3 + bx^2 + cx + d$, where a cannot be zero.

- The graph of the **reciprocal function** is of the form $y = \dfrac{a}{x}$, where x cannot be equal to zero.

- The graph of the **exponential function** is of the form $y = a^x$.

- The graph of a **circle**, centre $(0, 0)$, is of the form $x^2 + y^2 = r^2$, where r is the radius of the circle.

You should be able to identify and sketch the graphs of functions. For example:

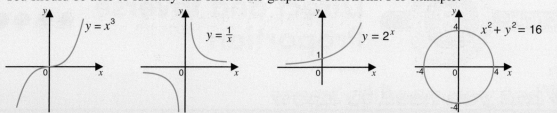

Exercise 17

1 (a) Draw the graph of $y = x^2 - 2$ for values of x from -3 to 3.
   (b) Write down the values of x at the points where the line $y = 3$ crosses your graph.
   (c) Use your graph to solve the equation $x^2 - 2 = 0$.

2 (a) Copy and complete the table for the equation $y = x^2 - 3x - 2$.

x	-1	0	1	2	3	4
y			-4	-4	-2	

   (b) Hence, draw the graph of $y = x^2 - 3x - 2$.
   (c) Use your graph to find the smallest value of y.
   (d) Use your graph to find the solutions of the equation $x^2 - 3x - 2 = 0$.   OCR

3 (a) Draw the graph of $y = 5x - x^2$ for $-1 \leqslant x \leqslant 6$.
   (b) Use your graph to solve the equation   (i) $5x - x^2 = 0$,   (ii) $5x - x^2 = 3$.

4 (a) Draw the graph of $y = 2x^2 - 3x + 2$ for values of x from -2 to 3.
   (b) Explain how the graph shows that there are no values of x for which $2x^2 - 3x + 2 = 0$.
   (c) State the minimum value of y.

5 (a) Copy and complete the table of values below for the equation $y = \dfrac{120}{x}$.

x	10	15	20	30	40	50	60
y						2.4	

   (b) Hence, draw the graph of $y = \dfrac{120}{x}$.
   (c) Use your graph to find the time to travel 120 km at a speed of 37 km/h.
   (d) Given that 1 gallon is equivalent to 4.5 litres, use your graph to find the number of gallons in 120 litres.   OCR

6 (a) Using the same axes, draw the graphs with equations $y = 3x$ and $y = x^2 + 1$.
   (b) Explain how you can use these graphs to solve the equation $x^2 - 3x + 1 = 0$.
   (c) Hence, solve the equation $x^2 - 3x + 1 = 0$.

7 (a) Draw the graph of $y = x^3 - x$ for $-3 \leqslant x \leqslant 3$.
   (b) Use your graph to find the value of x when $y = 10$.

8 On separate diagrams, sketch the graphs of these equations.
   Label any point where the graphs cross the x or y axes.
   (a) $y = -x^3$ (b) $xy = 4$ (c) $x^2 + y^2 = 9$

9 (a) Draw the graph of $y = 4^x$ for values of x from -2 to 2.
   (b) Use your graph to find the value of x when $y = 8$.

10 Find graphically the points of intersection of $x^2 + y^2 = 16$ and $2y = x - 1$.

Direct and Inverse Proportion

What you need to know

- **Direct proportion**
  If x and y are quantities such that $y : x^n$ is always constant, then y varies **directly** with x^n.
  This can be expressed:
  - in **words**: y is **proportional** to x^n,
  - in **symbols**: $y \alpha x^n$ (where α means "is proportional to"),
  - as an **equation**: $y = kx^n$ (where k is the **constant of proportionality**).

Eg 1 The cost, £C, of tiling a floor is proportional to the area of the floor, $a\,\text{m}^2$.
It costs £60 to tile a floor of area $2\,\text{m}^2$.
  (a) Find the formula connecting C and a.
  (b) A floor costs £150 to be tiled. What is the area of the floor?

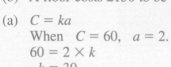

(a) $C = ka$
   When $C = 60$, $a = 2$.
   $60 = 2 \times k$
   $k = 30$
   $C = 30a$

(b) $C = 30a$
   When $C = 150$.
   $150 = 30a$
   $a = 5$
   Area of floor $= 5\,\text{m}^2$

> Constant of proportionality, k.
> This can be calculated when corresponding values of C and a are known.

- **Inverse proportion**
  If x and y are quantities such that $y : \dfrac{1}{x^n}$ is always constant, then y varies **inversely** with x^n.

  This can be expressed:
  - in **words**: y is **inversely proportional** to x^n,
  - in **symbols**: $y \alpha \dfrac{1}{x^n}$,
  - as an **equation**: $y = \dfrac{k}{x^n}$ or $x^n y = k$.

Eg 2 y is inversely proportional to x^2. When $x = 3$, $y = 4$.
  (a) Find the equation connecting y and x.   (b) Find the value of y when $x = 2.4$.

(a) $y = \dfrac{k}{x^2}$

   When $x = 3$, $y = 4$.

   $4 = \dfrac{k}{3^2}$, so, $k = 36$

   $y = \dfrac{36}{x^2}$

(b) $y = \dfrac{36}{x^2}$

   When $x = 2.4$.

   $y = \dfrac{36}{(2.4)^2}$

   $y = 6.25$

- The general form of a proportional relationship is $y \alpha x^n$ or $y = kx^n$.

Direct proportion, $y = kx^n$, $n > 0$

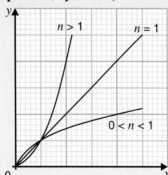

Inverse proportion, $y = kx^n$, $n < 0$

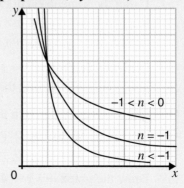

When:
  $n = 1$: y increases at a constant rate.
  $0 < n < 1$: y increases at a rate that decreases.
  $n > 1$: y increases at a rate that increases.

When:
  $n = -1$: the graph is symmetrical about the line $y = x$.

1 The table shows values of m and n.

m	0.6	9	16.5
n	0.4	6	11

(a) Show that m is directly proportional to n.

(b) Find the value of
   (i) m when $n = 1.8$,
   (ii) n when $m = 12.6$.

2 You are given that $T \alpha \dfrac{1}{R^2}$ and $T = 8$ when $R = 5$.

Find the equation connecting T and R. OCR

3 y is proportional to x^3.

When $x = 3$, $y = 54$.

Find the value of x when $y = 250$.

4 The cost, $£C$, of printing a film is proportional to the square of the width, w cm, of the prints.

$C = 1.60$ when $w = 8$.

(a) Express C in terms of w.

(b) Calculate w when $C = 3.60$. OCR

5 m is proportional to the square root of n.

$m = 6$ when $n = 81$.

(a) Find the equation connecting m and n.

(b) Calculate
   (i) the value of m when $n = 36$,
   (ii) the value of n when $m = 10$.

6 An artist hand-paints circular plates of different sizes.

The price, $£C$, of a hand-painted plate is proportional to the square of the radius, r cm, of the plate.

The price of a plate of radius 6 cm is £9.

Calculate the price of a plate of radius 8 cm.

7 (a)
 A   B   C   D   E   F

Choose which of the above graphs best represents each of these relationships.

(i) y is proportional to x,

(ii) y is proportional to x^2,

(iii) y is inversely proportional to x.

(b) When x takes a certain value, the value of $y = 10$.

If this value of x is multiplied by 4, work out the value of y when

(i) y is proportional to x,

(ii) y is proportional to x^2,

(iii) y is inversely proportional to x. OCR

8 You are given that $y = 6x^n$ and that $y = 3$ when $x = 8$.

Find the value of n.

Quadratic Equations

What you need to know

● Brackets, such as $(x + 2)(x + 3)$, can be multiplied out using the **diagram method**, or by **expanding**.

Eg 1 Multiply out $(x + 2)(x + 3)$.

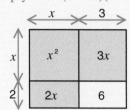

$$(x + 2)(x + 3) = x^2 + 3x + 2x + 6$$
$$= x^2 + 5x + 6$$

Eg 2 Expand $(x - 3)(2x + 1)$.

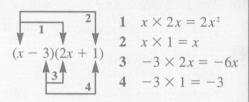

1   $x \times 2x = 2x^2$
2   $x \times 1 = x$
3   $-3 \times 2x = -6x$
4   $-3 \times 1 = -3$

$$(x - 3)(2x + 1) = 2x^2 + x - 6x - 3$$
$$= 2x^2 - 5x - 3$$

● **Factorising** is the opposite operation to removing brackets.

Eg 3 Factorise the following.
  (a) $x^2 + 3x = x(x + 3)$
  (b) $2x^2 - 8 = 2(x^2 - 4)$
            $= 2(x - 2)(x + 2)$
  (c) $x^2 + 2x - 15 = (x + 5)(x - 3)$

> When factorising, work logically.
> 1. Does the expression have a **common factor**?
> 2. Is the expression a **difference of two squares**?
> $a^2 - b^2 = (a - b)(a + b)$
> 3. Will the expression factorise into **two brackets**?

● Some **quadratic equations** can be solved by factorising.

Eg 4 Solve these equations.
  (a) $x^2 - 5x = 0$
      $x(x - 5) = 0$
      $x = 0$ or $x = 5$

  (b) $m^2 + m - 6 = 0$
      $(m - 2)(m + 3) = 0$
      $m = 2$ or $m = -3$

  (c) $2a^2 - 5a - 3 = 0$
      $(2a + 1)(a - 3) = 0$
      $a = -\frac{1}{2}$ or $a = 3$

● The general form for a **quadratic equation** is $ax^2 + bx + c = 0$ where a cannot be zero.

● The solutions to a quadratic equation can be found using the **quadratic formula**.

> If $ax^2 + bx + c = 0$ and $a \neq 0$ then $x = \dfrac{-b \pm \sqrt{b^2 - 4ac}}{2a}$

Eg 5 Solve $x^2 - 3x - 2 = 0$.

$$x = \frac{-(-3) \pm \sqrt{(-3)^2 - 4(1)(-2)}}{2(1)}$$

$$x = \frac{3 \pm \sqrt{17}}{2}$$

$x = -0.56$ or $x = 3.56$,   correct to two decimal places.

> Substitute: $a = 1$, $b = -3$ and $c = -2$,
> into $x = \dfrac{-b \pm \sqrt{b^2 - 4ac}}{2a}$

● Quadratic expressions, such as $x^2 + 8x + 20$, can be written in the form $(x + a)^2 + b$, where a and b are integers.

> In **completed square form**, $(x + a)^2 + b$:
> the value of a is half the coefficient of x, the
> value of b is found by subtracting the value of a^2
> from the constant term of the original expression.

Eg 6 $x^2 + 8x + 20 = (x + a)^2 + b$
          $a = \frac{1}{2}(8) = 4$
          $b = 20 - 4^2 = 4$
          $x^2 + 8x + 20 = (x + 4)^2 + 4$

- Quadratic equations can be solved by **completing the square**.

Eg 7 Solve $x^2 + 4x = 5$.
$(x + 2)^2 - 4 = 5$
$(x + 2)^2 = 9$
$x + 2 = \pm 3$
$x + 2 = 3$ or $x + 2 = -3$
$x = 1$ or $x = -5$

> Write the left-hand side (LHS) of the equation in the form $(x + a)^2 + b$ by completing the square.
> $x^2 + 4x = (x + 2)^2 - 4$

- You should be able to form and solve quadratic equations.

Exercise 19

1 Multiply out and simplify. (a) $x(x - 7)$ (b) $(x - 2)(x + 5)$

2 Remove brackets and simplify where possible.
(a) $x(4x^2 - 3)$ (b) $(x + 3)(2x - 1)$ OCR

3 Factorise.
(a) $x^2 - 4x$ (b) $x^2 + 2x - 15$ (c) $x^2 - 4x + 3$ (d) $x^2 - 9$

4 Solve these equations.
(a) $x(x + 5) = 0$ (b) $(x - 3)(x + 2) = 0$ (c) $(2x + 3)(x - 1) = 0$

5 (a) Multiply out the brackets and simplify $(2x + 3)(2x - 3)$.
(b) Factorise (i) $x^2 + 6x$,   (ii) $x^2 + 6x + 8$.
(c) Solve the equation $(x - 3)(x + 5) = 0$.   OCR

6 (a) Solve the equation $x^2 + 3x = 0$.
(b) Factorise $x^2 - 7x + 12$.   OCR

7 (a) Factorise. $x^2 - 5x + 6$
(b) Solve this equation. $x^2 - 5x + 6 = 0$ OCR

8 A rectangle has sides of length $x + 1$ and $x + 2$.
The area of the rectangle is 42.
Form an equation in x and solve it to find x.

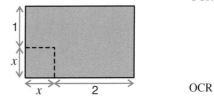

OCR

9 (a) Factorise $2x^2 - 5x - 3 = 0$.
(b) Hence, solve the equation $2x^2 - 5x - 3 = 0$.

10 Solve the equation $3x^2 - x - 2 = 0$.

11 Express in the form $x^2 + bx + c = 0$
the quadratic equation which has solutions $x = 2$ and $x = -3$.

12 (a) Write $x^2 - 4x - 8$ in the form $(x + a)^2 + b$.
(b) Hence, solve the equation $x^2 - 4x - 8 = 0$, correct to 2 decimal places.

13 Solve the equation $x^2 + 3x - 5 = 0$.

14 Solve the equation $x^2 = 3x + 5$, giving your answers correct to 3 significant figures.

15 Solve the equation $2x^2 - x - 2 = 0$.

16 The area of a rectangle, with dimensions x cm by $(x + 2)$ cm, is 18 cm².
Calculate the value of x, correct to one decimal place.

What you need to know

- A pair of **simultaneous equations** has the same unknown letters in each equation.

- To solve a pair of simultaneous equations find values for the unknown letters that fit **both** equations.

- Simultaneous equations can be solved either **graphically** or **algebraically**.

- Solving simultaneous equations **graphically** involves:
  drawing the graphs of both equations,
  finding the point(s) where the graphs cross.
  When the graphs of both equations are parallel, the equations have no solution.

  Eg 1 Solve the simultaneous equations $x + 2y = 5$ and $x - 2y = 1$ graphically.

  Draw the graph of $x + 2y = 5$.
  Draw the graph of $x - 2y = 1$.

  The lines cross at the point (3, 1).
  This gives the solution $x = 3$ and $y = 1$.

  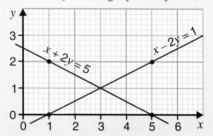

- Solving simultaneous equations **algebraically** involves using either:
  the **elimination** method, or the **substitution** method.

  Eg 2 Solve the simultaneous equations $5x + 2y = 11$ and $3x - 4y = 4$ algebraically.

  $$5x + 2y = 11 \quad \text{A}$$
  $$3x - 4y = 4 \quad \text{B}$$

  A × 2 gives $\quad 10x + 4y = 22 \quad$ C $\qquad$ | To make the number of y's the same
  $\qquad\qquad\qquad 3x - 4y = 4 \quad$ D $\qquad$ | we can multiply equation A by 2.

  C + D gives $\qquad\qquad 13x = 26 \qquad$ | The number of y's is the **same** but the **signs** are **different**.
  $\qquad\qquad\qquad\quad x = 2 \qquad$ | To eliminate the y's the equations must be **added**.

  Substitute $x = 2$ into $5x + 2y = 11$.
  $$10 + 2y = 11$$
  $$2y = 1$$
  $$y = 0.5 \qquad$$ | You can check the solution by substituting
  The solution is $x = 2$ and $y = 0.5$. $\qquad$ | $x = 2$ and $y = 0.5$ into $3x - 4y = 4$.

- You should be able to solve simultaneous equations in which one equation is linear and one is quadratic.

  Eg 3 Solve the simultaneous equations $y = x - 2$ and $x^2 + 3y = 12$.

  Substitute $y = x - 2$ into $x^2 + 3y = 12$. $\qquad$ | Using $y = x - 2$.
  $x^2 + 3(x - 2) = 12$ $\qquad\qquad\qquad\qquad$ | When $x = -6$. $\qquad$ When $x = 3$.
  $x^2 + 3x - 18 = 0$ $\qquad\qquad\qquad\qquad$ | $y = -6 - 2$ $\qquad\qquad$ $y = 3 - 2$
  $(x + 6)(x - 3) = 0$ $\qquad\qquad\qquad\qquad$ | $y = -8$ $\qquad\qquad\qquad$ $y = 1$
  $x = -6$ or $x = 3$

  This gives the solution: $x = -6$, $y = -8$ **and** $x = 3$, $y = 1$.

1 (a) On the same axes, draw the graphs of $y + x = 4$ and $y - 3x = 2$
   for values of x from -2 to 2.
   (b) Hence, solve the simultaneous equations $y + x = 4$ and $y - 3x = 2$.

2 Solve graphically the simultaneous equations $y = 3 - x$ and $y = x - 2$.

3 The sketch shows the graph of $y = 2x - 1$.
   Copy the diagram.
   (a) On your diagram, sketch the graph of $y = 2x + 1$.
   (b) Explain why the equations $y = 2x - 1$ and $y = 2x + 1$
      cannot be solved simultaneously.

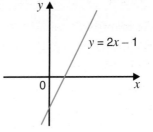

4 Solve these simultaneous equations. $6x + y = 7$
   $\qquad\qquad\qquad\qquad\qquad\qquad 2x - y = -3$

5 Solve the simultaneous equations $5x + 4y = 13$
   $\qquad\qquad\qquad\qquad\qquad\qquad\qquad 3x + 8y = 5.$ 　　　　　　　OCR

6 Solve the simultaneous equations $x + 3y = 13$ and $4x + 2y = 2$.

7 Solve, algebraically, these simultaneous equations. $3x - y = 1$
   $\qquad\qquad\qquad\qquad\qquad\qquad\qquad\qquad\qquad x + 2y = 12$ 　　　OCR

8 Heather sold 40 boxes of cards to raise money for charity.
   She sold x small boxes at £4 each and y large boxes at £7 each.
   She raised £184 altogether.
   (a) Write down two equations connecting x and y.
   (b) Solve these simultaneous equations to find how many of each size of box she sold.

9 Micro-scooters costs £x each and pogo sticks cost £y each.
   2 micro-scooters and 4 pogo sticks cost £65.
   1 micro-scooter and 3 pogo sticks cost £40.
   (a) Write down two equations connecting x and y.
   (b) Solve these simultaneous equations to find the cost of a micro-scooter and a pogo stick.

10 Solve these simultaneous equations algebraically. $4x + 3y = 6$
   $\qquad\qquad\qquad\qquad\qquad\qquad\qquad\qquad\qquad 3x - 2y = 13$ 　　　OCR

11 Solve the simultaneous equations $2x + 3y = 7$ and $3x - 2y = 17$.

12 Use a graphical method to solve each of these pairs of simultaneous equations.
   (a) $y = 4 - 2x$ 　　　　　(b) $y - x = 4$ 　　　　　(c) $y = 2x$
   　　$y = x^2 - 4$ 　　　　　　　$y = 6x - x^2$ 　　　　　　$x^2 + y^2 = 25$

13 Use an algebraic method to solve the simultaneous equations $5y = 2x - 7$ and $xy = 6$.

14 (a) On a pair of axes sketch the graphs of $y = 3 - x$ and $y = 2x^2$.
      Do not draw the graphs accurately.
   (b) Use algebra to find the coordinates of the points where the graphs cross. 　　OCR

15 Solve the simultaneous equations.
   (a) $y - x = -11$ 　　　　(b) $y = 3 - x$ 　　　　(c) $2x + y = 3$
   　　$x^2 = y + 13$ 　　　　　　$x^2 + y^2 = 17$ 　　　　　$y = \dfrac{1}{x}$

16 The straight line with equation $y = x + 6$ meets the circle with equation $x^2 + y^2 = 50$
   at two points, P and Q.
   By solving two simultaneous equations, find the coordinates of P and Q. 　　OCR

Algebraic Methods

What you need to know

- An **identity** is true for all values of x. It is the same expression written in another form.
  For example: $(2x + 3)^2 + (2x + 9)(2x + 5) = 2(4x^2 + 20x + 27)$.

  > To show that an identity is true, either:
  > start with the LHS and show that it is equal to the RHS, or
  > start with the RHS and show that it is equal to the LHS.

- **Algebraic fractions** have a numerator and a denominator.

  > To write an algebraic fraction in its **simplest form**:
  > factorise the numerator and denominator of the fraction, divide
  > the numerator and denominator by their highest common factor.

  Eg 1 Simplify.

  (a) $\dfrac{2x - 4}{x^2 - 2x} = \dfrac{2(x - 2)}{x(x - 2)} = \dfrac{2}{x}$

  (b) $\dfrac{x^2 - 9}{x^2 + 2x - 3} = \dfrac{(x + 3)(x - 3)}{(x + 3)(x - 1)} = \dfrac{(x - 3)}{(x - 1)}$

  > The same methods used for adding,
  > subtracting, multiplying and
  > dividing numeric fractions can be
  > applied to algebraic fractions.

  (c) $\dfrac{2}{x - 3} - \dfrac{1}{x} = \dfrac{2x - (x - 3)}{x(x - 3)} = \dfrac{x + 3}{x(x - 3)}$

- You should be able to solve equations involving algebraic fractions.

- The solutions to a variety of equations can be found using a process called **iteration**.

  > The process of iteration has three stages.
  > **1.** Rearranging an equation to form an **iterative formula**.
  > **2.** Choosing a **starting value**, x_1.
  > **3.** **Substituting** the starting value, and then values of x_n into the iterative formula.
  > Continuing the process until the required degree of accuracy is obtained.

  Eg 2 Find a solution to the equation $x^2 - 4x - 3 = 0$, correct to 2 decimal places, using iteration.

  Use the iterative formula $x_{n + 1} = \sqrt{4x_n + 3}$.

  $$x_1 = 4$$
  $$x_2 = \sqrt{4 \times 4 + 3} = 4.3588\ldots$$
  $$x_3 = \sqrt{4 \times 4.3588\ldots + 3} = 4.5205\ldots$$
  $$x_4 = \sqrt{4 \times 4.5205\ldots + 3} = 4.5915\ldots$$
  $$x_5 = \sqrt{4 \times 4.5915\ldots + 3} = 4.6223\ldots$$
  $$x_6 = \sqrt{4 \times 4.6223\ldots + 3} = 4.6356\ldots$$
  $$x_7 = \sqrt{4 \times 4.6356\ldots + 3} = 4.6414\ldots$$
  $$x_8 = \sqrt{4 \times 4.6414\ldots + 3} = 4.6438\ldots$$

  $$x = 4.64, \text{ correct to 2 d.p.}$$

- **Trial and improvement** is a method used to solve equations. The accuracy of the value of the unknown letter is improved until the required degree of accuracy is obtained.

Eg 3 Use a trial and improvement method to find a solution to the equation $x^3 + x = 40$, correct to one decimal place.

x	$x^3 + x$	Comment
3	$27 + 3 = 30$	Too small
4	$64 + 4 = 68$	Too big
3.5	$42.8\ldots + 3.5 = 46.3\ldots$	Too big
3.3	$35.9\ldots + 3.3 = 39.2\ldots$	Too small
3.35	$37.5\ldots + 3.35 = 40.9\ldots$	Too big

For accuracy to 1 d.p. check the second decimal place. The solution lies between 3.3 and 3.35.

$x = 3.3$, correct to 1 d.p.

Exercise 21

1 Expand and simplify $(x + 3)^2 - (x - 3)^2$.

2 Show that $2x(x + y) - (x + y)^2 = x^2 - y^2$.

3 Simplify. (a) $\dfrac{x^2 - 3x}{x}$ (b) $\dfrac{2x^2 - 6x}{4x - 12}$ (c) $\dfrac{x^2 + 2x + 1}{x^2 - 2x - 3}$ (d) $\dfrac{x^2 + x}{x^2 - 1}$

4 (a) Factorise. $x^2 - 4y^2$

(b) Simplify. $\dfrac{x^2 - 4y^2}{5x + 10y}$ OCR

5 Simplify. (a) $\dfrac{1}{x} + \dfrac{1}{2x}$ (b) $\dfrac{2x}{x + 1} + \dfrac{1}{2}$ (c) $\dfrac{1}{x + 2} + \dfrac{2}{2x - 5}$

6 (a) Simplify this expression. $\dfrac{x^2 + 5x}{x^2 + 2x - 15}$

(b) Write this expression as a single fraction, simplifying the numerator. $\dfrac{3}{x + 2} - \dfrac{5}{2x + 1}$ OCR

7 (a) Simplify this expression. $\dfrac{x^2 - 9}{x^2 + x - 6}$

(b) Use algebra to solve this equation. $\dfrac{12}{3x + 1} - \dfrac{5}{x + 1} = 1$ OCR

8 (a) Show that $y = \dfrac{3}{2x - 1} - \dfrac{2}{x + 3}$ can be written as $y = \dfrac{11 - x}{2x^2 + 5x - 3}$.

(b) Hence, find the values of x when $y = 1$, correct to 2 decimal places.

9 Solve the equation $\dfrac{x}{2} - \dfrac{3}{x + 5} = 1$.

10 Solve the equation $\dfrac{2}{2x - 1} - 1 = \dfrac{2}{x + 1}$.

11 (a) (i) Factorise $3x^2 - 8x - 3$.

(ii) Hence, or otherwise, simplify $\dfrac{9x^2 - 1}{3x^2 - 8x - 3}$.

(b) Solve the equation $\dfrac{1}{1 - x} - \dfrac{1}{1 + x} = 1$.

12 (a) Show that one solution of the equation $x^3 - 5x - 8 = 0$ lies between 2 and 3.

(b) Use trial and improvement to find this solution, correct to one decimal place. You must show all your trials and their outcomes. OCR

13 Use a trial and improvement method to find the value of x, correct to **one** decimal place, when $x^3 - 3x = 38$. Show clearly your trials and their outcomes. OCR

Transforming Graphs

What you need to know

- **Function notation** is a way of expressing a relationship between two variables.
  For example

  Input, x → | function, f
 e.g. *cube* | → Output, f(x)

  This notation gives $f(x) = x^3$

  f(x) means 'a function of x'.
  In the example above, $f(x) = x^3$ is equivalent to the equation $y = x^3$ where $y = f(x)$.

- **Transformations**, such as **translations** and **stretches**, can be used to change the position and size of a graph.
  The equation of the transformed (new) graph is related to the equation of the original graph.

  In general

Original	New graph	Transformation	Note
$y = f(x)$	$y = f(x) + a$	**translation**, vector $\begin{pmatrix} 0 \\ a \end{pmatrix}$.	If a is **positive**, curve moves a units **up**. If a is **negative**, curve moves a units **down**.
$y = f(x)$	$y = f(x + a)$	**translation**, vector $\begin{pmatrix} -a \\ 0 \end{pmatrix}$.	If a is **positive**, curve moves a units **left**. If a is **negative**, curve moves a units **right**.
$y = f(x)$	$y = af(x)$	**stretch**, from the x axis, parallel to the y axis, scale factor a.	The y coordinates on the graph of $y = f(x)$ are **multiplied** by a.
$y = f(x)$	$y = f(ax)$	**stretch**, from the y axis, parallel to the x axis, scale factor $\frac{1}{a}$.	The x coordinates on the graph of $y = f(x)$ are **divided** by a.
$y = f(x)$	$y = -f(x)$	**reflection** in the x axis.	The y coordinates on the graph of $y = f(x)$ **change signs**.
$y = f(x)$	$y = f(-x)$	**reflection** in the y axis.	The x coordinates on the graph of $y = f(x)$ **change signs**.

Eg 1 The diagram shows the graph of $y = f(x)$.
Draw the graphs of $y = f(x - 2)$ and $y = f(x) - 2$.

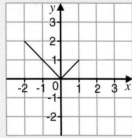 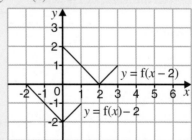

- You should be able to draw a suitable graph to find the relationship between a given set of variables.
  Linear functions have straight line graphs, such as $y = ax + b$.
  From the graph of **y against x**, the gradient $= a$ and   the y-intercept $= b$.
  Non-linear functions, such as $y = ax^n + b$,   can be written as the linear function $y = az + b$
  by substituting $z = x^n$.
  From the graph of **y against x^n**, the gradient $= a$ and   the y-intercept $= b$.

1 The graph of $y = f(x)$ for $-2 \leqslant x \leqslant 2$ is shown.
On separate diagrams draw the graphs of $y = f(x)$ and:

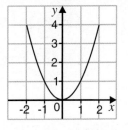

(a) $y = f(x + 2)$,

(b) $y = f(x) + 2$,

(c) $y = 2f(x)$,

(d) $y = -f(x)$.

2

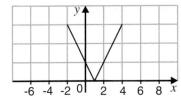

The graph of $y = f(x)$ for $-2 \leqslant x \leqslant 4$ is drawn on the grid.

On separate grids

(a) Sketch the graph of $y = 2f(x)$,

(b) Sketch the graph of $y = f(x - 2)$.　　OCR

3 This diagram shows the graph of $y = f(x)$.

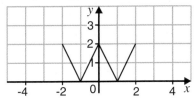

The two graphs below are transformations of $y = f(x)$.

(a)

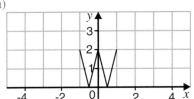

(b)

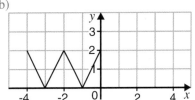

Choose the correct equation for each graph.

$y = f(x + 2)$　　　$y = f\left(\frac{x}{2}\right)$　　　$y = f(x - 2)$　　　$y = \frac{1}{2} f(x)$

$y = f(2x)$　　　$y = f(x) - 2$　　　$y = 2f(x)$　　　$y = f(x) + 2$　　　OCR

4 The diagram shows a sketch of the graph of $y = f(x)$ for $-2 \leqslant x \leqslant 2$.

Each of the graphs below is a transformation of this graph.
Write down the equation of each graph.

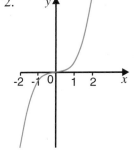

(a)

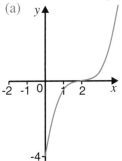

(b)

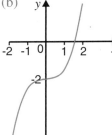

(c)

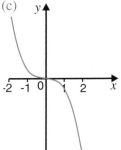

5 The table shows the values of x and y recorded during an experiment.

x	1	2	3	4	5
y	14	21	37	57	87

(a) Plot the graph of y against x^2 and draw a line of best fit.

(b) Use your graph to find an equation that approximately connects y and x^2.　　OCR

Algebra
Non-calculator Paper

Do not use a calculator for this exercise.

1 (a) Simplify. $3x + 4y + 7x - 5y$

(b) Multiply out the brackets. $5(7 - 2x)$

OCR

2 (a) (i) Copy and complete the table for $y = 3x - 1$.

x	0	1	2	3	4
y					

(ii) Draw the graph of $y = 3x - 1$.

(b) (i) Copy and complete the table for $y = x^2 - 1$.

x	0	1	2	3	4
y		0		8	

(ii) Draw the graph of $y = x^2 - 1$ on the same grid as (a).

OCR

3 Hannah is x years old.

(a) Her sister Louisa is 3 years younger than Hannah.
Write an expression, in terms of x, for Louisa's age.

(b) Their mother is four times as old as Hannah.
Write an expression, in terms of x, for their mother's age.

(c) The total of their ages is 45 years.
By forming an equation in x, find their ages.

4 Given that $S = ut + \frac{1}{2}t^2$, find S when $u = -30$ and $t = 4$.

OCR

5 Ken drives from his home to the city centre.
The graph represents his journey.

(a) How long did Ken take to reach the city centre?

(b) How far from the city centre does Ken live?

(c) What is his average speed for the journey in kilometres per hour?

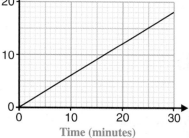

6 (a) Factorise (i) $3a - 6$, (ii) $k^2 - 2k$.

(b) Cynthia has x five pound notes and $2x$ ten pound notes.
Write an expression, in terms of x, for the total value of her notes.

7 Solve. (a) $2x = 7$ (b) $3x - 5 = 13$ (c) $6x - 9 = x + 26$

OCR

8 Given that $s = 2t^3$, find the value of t when $s = 250$.

9 (a) Expand. $x(x + 2)$

(b) Multiply out the brackets and simplify. $3(4x + 1) + 2(2x - 1)$

(c) (i) Solve. $2x - 5 \geqslant 4$

(ii) Show your solution to part (i) on a number line.

OCR

10 (a) $y = \frac{4}{5}(9 - x)$. Find the value of x when $y = 6$.

(b) Solve the equation $\frac{3x + 5}{2} = 7$.

11 The nth term of a sequence is $2n^2 + 5$. Find the 10th term of this sequence.

12 Tickets for a concert cost either £10 or £15.
300 people attended the concert. x people paid £15 for their ticket.
(a) Write down an expression in x for the amount of money taken for £10 tickets.

The 300 people paid £3950 in total for their tickets.
(b) Write down an equation in x and solve it to find out how many people paid £15. OCR

13 (a) Solve the equation. $5(x + 2) = x + 20$
(b) (i) Write down the integer values of n for which $1 < 3n \leqslant 12$.
(ii) Solve the inequality $5x - 2 \geqslant 1$. OCR

14 Match these equations to their graphs.

A $y = x$
B $y + x = 1$
C $y = x^2$
D $y = x^3$

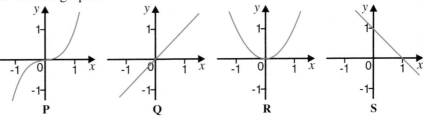

P   Q   R   S

15 (a) Find the first and second term of this sequence. ..., ..., 5, 9, 13, 17
(b) Find a formula for the n th term of this sequence. OCR

16 (a) Copy and complete the table of values for $y = x^2 - 2x + 1$.

x	-1	0	1	2	3
y		1	0		4

(b) Draw the graph of $y = x^2 - 2x + 1$ for values of x from -1 to 3.
(c) Use your graph to solve the equations
(i) $x^2 - 2x + 1 = 0$,
(ii) $x^2 - 2x + 1 = 2$.

17 Water is poured into a container at a constant rate.
Copy the axes given and sketch the graph of the
depth of the water against time as the container is filled.

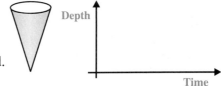

18 (a) Solve $5(x + 1) = 3x + 14$.
(b) Expand and simplify $4(5x - 2) - 2(2x - 1)$. OCR

19 Solve. (a) $\dfrac{9x - 15}{4} = x$ (b) $3(2x - 1) - 2(x - 4) = 19$ OCR

20 (a) Find the gradient of this line.

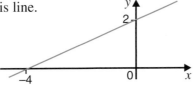

(b) The equation of a different line is $4y - 3x = 8$. What is the gradient of this line?

21 Write each of these expressions as a single power of y.
(a) $y^2 \times y^3$ (b) $\dfrac{y^8}{y^2}$ (c) $(y^4)^2$. OCR

22 (a) Solve the inequality $9n + 1 < 14n - 2$.
(b) Multiply out the brackets and simplify $(x + 3)(2x - 1)$.
(c) Factorise $x^2 - 3x - 4$.
(d) Rearrange the formula $s = \frac{1}{2} gt^2$ to make t the subject. OCR

23 (a) (i) Factorise. $x^2 + 9x + 20$
       (ii) Solve. $\quad x^2 + 9x + 20 = 0$

   (b) Solve, algebraically, these simultaneous equations.
      $14x + 3y = 1$ and $4x - y = 4$ OCR

24 (a) Solve the equations   (i) $x(x + 2) = 0$,   (ii) $y^2 - 3y + 2 = 0$.

   (b) Expand and simplify $(2x - 3)(x + 2)$.

25 (a) Make e the subject of the formula $2(e - 2d) = 4d - 1$.

   (b) Solve the equation $x^2 - 6x + 8 = 0$.   OCR

26 Simplify.   (a) $(3x^2y)^3$ (b) $\dfrac{3a^2b^3 \times 4a^5b}{6a^3b^2}$

27 Factorise the following.   (a) $3x^2 - 75$ (b) $3x^2 - 8x + 5$

28 Make a the subject of the formula $6(a + 2b) = 4a + 7$.   OCR

29 This diagram shows the graph of the function $y = f(x)$.
Draw sketch graphs of the following functions.

   (a) $y = f(x + 2)$

   (b) $y = f(x) + 2$

   (c) $y = 2f(x)$

   (d) $y = f(2x)$

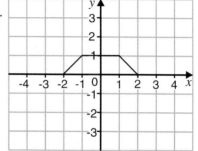

30 P is directly proportional to the square root of q.
When $P = 15$ then $q = 9$.

   (a) Work out a formula to connect P and q.

   (b) Work out the value of q when $P = 4$.   OCR

31 Simplify.   (a) $\dfrac{3}{x - 1} - \dfrac{2}{x + 1}$ (b) $\dfrac{x^2 - 9}{x^2 + x - 12}$ OCR

32 (a) Show that $(2x + 3)^2 - (2x + 1)^2 = 8(x + 1)$.

   (b) Hence, solve the equation $(2x + 3)^2 - (2x + 1)^2 = x^2 - 1$.

33 Rearrange the equation $x = \dfrac{y - 5}{3 - y}$ to make y the subject.

34 The speed-time graph of an underground train
travelling between two stations is shown.

   (a) What is the maximum speed of the train?

   (b) Calculate the acceleration of the train.

   (c) Calculate the distance between the stations.

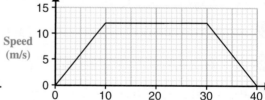

35 Find the equation of the line which is perpendicular to
$2y + x = 6$ and goes through the point $(4, 1)$.

36 Write each of the following as a single fraction as simply as possible.

   (a) $\dfrac{a}{bc} - \dfrac{b}{ac}$ (b) $\dfrac{b^{0.5}}{a^{-3}} \div \dfrac{a^2}{b^{1.5}}$

37 By completing the square, find the coordinates of the minimum point of $y = x^2 + 8x + 7$.
           OCR

38 Solve the simultaneous equations $y = 2x + 1$ and $xy = 3$.

39 You are given that $\dfrac{1}{x + 1} - \dfrac{3}{2x - 1} = 2$.

Show that $4x^2 + 3x + 2 = 0$.

Algebra
Calculator Paper

You may use a calculator for this exercise.

1 (a) In a week, Phil makes 5 journeys each of length x miles and 8 journeys each of length y miles.
Write down an expression for the number of miles Phil travels in a week.

(b) Find the value of $\dfrac{3a + 5b}{4}$ when $a = 9$ and $b = -3$. OCR

2 (a) $T = 3m - 5$. Find the value of m when $T = 4$.
(b) $P = 5y^2$. Find the value of P when $y = 3$.

3 The distance-time graph below shows a journey between Alex's house and Craig's house.

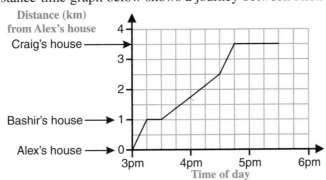

Alex walked from his home to Bashir's house, then they walked together to Craig's house.
(a) How long did Alex spend at Bashir's house?
(b) How far were they from Bashir's house at 4 pm?
(c) What happened at 4.30 pm?
(d) At 5.30 pm, Craig's mother drove Alex home.
He arrived home at 5.45 pm.
Calculate the average speed of Alex's car journey. OCR

4 The n th term of a sequence is $2n^2 + 1$.
(a) Find the first term.
(b) Tom says that the fifth term is 101. Explain why he is wrong. OCR

5 (a) Solve the equations (i) $4(a - 2) = 6$,   (ii) $5t + 3 = -1 + t$.
(b) The sum of the numbers x, $x - 3$ and $x + 7$ is 25.
By forming an equation in x, find the value of x.

6 Pali's wages each week for his job are made up of two parts.
                    ***Basic pay:* £227   *Overtime:* £9 per hour**
(a) One week, Pali works n hours overtime.
Write down an expression for his total wages this week.
(b) Another week, he was paid £299.
Write down an equation in n and solve it to find out how many extra hours he worked that week. OCR

7 (a) Draw the line $y = 2x + 1$ for values of x from -1 to 2.
(b) The line $y = 2x + 1$ crosses the line $x = -5$ at P.
Give the coordinates of P.

8 (a) Factorise. (i) $10x + 15$ (ii) $x^2 - 3x$
(b) Solve. $2(5x + 3) = 23$ OCR

9 (a) Write down the next two numbers in this sequence. 26   19   12   5   ...   ...

    (b) Here are the first five terms of another sequence. 5   8   11   14   17
       Find the n th term of this sequence.

10 The equation $x^3 + 8x - 40 = 0$ has a solution between 2 and 3.
Use trial and improvement to find this solution.
Give your answer correct to two decimal places.
Show clearly the outcomes of your trials.   OCR

11 (a) Copy and complete the table of values for $y = x^2 - 5$.

x	-3	-2	-1	0	1	2	3
y	4		-4	-5			4

    (b) Draw the graph of $y = x^2 - 5$ for values of x from -3 to 3.
    (c) Use your graph to solve the equation $x^2 - 5 = 0$.

12 (a) Multiply out the brackets and simplify this expression. $3(2x + 3) + 2(4x - 1)$
    (b) Rearrange the formula $P = 2L + 2W$ to make L the subject.   OCR

13 A glass of milk costs x pence. A milk shake costs 45 pence more than a glass of milk.
    (a) Write an expression for the cost of a milk shake.
    (b) Lou has to pay £4.55 for 3 milk shakes and a glass of milk.
       By forming an equation, find the price of a glass of milk.

14 (a) Solve the inequality $3x - 5 > 4$.
    (b) List the values of x, where x is an integer, such that $-1 \leqslant x + 2 < 1$.

15 (a) Simplify. $a^3 \times a^4$
    (b) Rearrange the formula $P = 3t + 5$ to find a formula for t in terms of P.   OCR

16 Use a trial and improvement method to find the value of x, correct to **one** decimal place,
when $x^3 - 2x = 68$. You must show all your trials.   OCR

17 (a) Solve the equation $3 - x = 4(x + 1)$.
    (b) Multiply out and simplify $2(5x - 3) - 3(x - 1)$.
    (c) Simplify (i) $m^8 \div m^2$,   (ii) $n^2 \times n^3$.

18 (a) Write down the equations of the lines labelled **A**, **B** and **C** in the diagram.
    (b) Write down three inequalities to describe the shaded region.

19 (a) Simplify. $(p^3 q^4) \times (p^5 q^3)$
    (b) Factorise completely.
       (i) $p^3 r^4 + p^5 r^3$ (ii) $25p^2 - 4q^2$
    (c) Rearrange this formula to make r the subject.
$$p = \frac{3(r^2 - 4)}{2}$$
                                        OCR

20 Solve the equation $\dfrac{5x - 3}{3} - \dfrac{1 + 2x}{2} = 3$

21 The diagram shows points A (2, 0), B (0, 2) and C (3, 5).
Find the equations of the line segments.
    (a) AB,   (b) BC,   (c) AC.

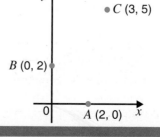

22 When a tuned guitar string is plucked it vibrates and produces a musical note. The frequency, f Hz, of the note produced is inversely proportional to the vibrating length, L cm, of the string. The sketch graph shows this relationship.

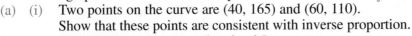

Frequency f Hz

Vibrating length L cm

   (a) (i) Two points on the curve are $(40, 165)$ and $(60, 110)$. Show that these points are consistent with inverse proportion.

        (ii) State the formula connecting f and L.

   (b) Calculate the length of string needed to produce a note of frequency 147 Hz.   OCR

23

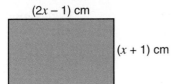

(2x – 1) cm

(x + 1) cm

The dimensions of a rectangle are shown. The rectangle has an area of 104 cm². Form an equation for the area of the rectangle and show that it can be written in the form $2x^2 + x - 105 = 0$.

24 Solve the equation $x^2 + 2x - 5 = 0$. Give your answers correct to two decimal places.

25 The volumes of these cuboids are the same.

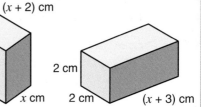

(x + 2) cm

3 cm

2 cm

x cm

2 cm

2 cm

(x + 3) cm

   (a) Show that $3x^2 + 2x - 12 = 0$.

   (b) By solving the equation $3x^2 + 2x - 12 = 0$, find the value of x. Give your answer correct to one decimal place.

26 (a) Draw the graph of $y = 3 - 2x^2$ for values of x between -2 and 2.

   (b) Use your graph to solve these equations. (i) $3 - 2x^2 = 0$ (ii) $3 - 2x^2 = x$

   (c) A student wants to use the graph to solve the equation $2x^2 - x - 2 = 0$. What is the equation of the line that needs to be drawn?

27 (a) Solve this equation. $2x^2 - 9x - 3 = 0$ Give your answers correct to three significant figures.

   (b) Rearrange the following formula to give a in terms of b. $b = \dfrac{8a + 4}{3 - 5a}$ OCR

28 Solve the equation $2x^2 = 5x - 1$.

29 You are given that $y = 8x^n$ and that $y = 1$ when $x = 2$. Find the value of n.

30 (a) Simplify fully the expression $\dfrac{2x^2 - 18}{2x^2 - 4x - 6}$.

   (b) You are given the equation $xy = x + y$. Rearrange the equation to give a formula for y in terms of x.

   (c) You are given that $(2x - b)^2 - 5 = ax^2 - 4x + c$ for all values of x. Find the values of a, b and c.

31 Solve the simultaneous equations $x + y = 4$ and $y = x^2 + 2x$.

32 (a) (i) Find the values of a and b when $x^2 - 6x + a = (x + b)^2$.

        (ii) Use your answer to (a)(i) to find the minimum value of $x^2 - 6x + 11$.

   (b) Prove. $\dfrac{x - 1}{x} - \dfrac{x}{x + 1} = \dfrac{-1}{x(x + 1)}$ OCR

33 (a) You are given that $(x + p)^2 + q = x^2 - 4x + 7$. Find the values of p and q.

   (b) Rearrange the equation $y(x - 3) = 1 + 2x$ to give a formula for x in terms of y.

34 Solve the equation $\dfrac{2}{x - 1} - \dfrac{1}{x + 1} = 1$.

Angles and 2-D Shapes

What you need to know

- Types and names of angles.

Acute angle	Right angle	Obtuse angle	Reflex angle
			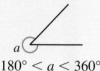
$0° < a < 90°$	$a = 90°$	$90° < a < 180°$	$180° < a < 360°$

- Angle properties.

Angles at a point	Complementary angles	Supplementary angles	Vertically opposite angles
		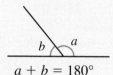	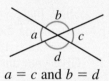
$a + b + c = 360°$	$x + y = 90°$	$a + b = 180°$	$a = c$ and $b = d$

- A straight line joining two points is called a **line segment**.

- Lines which meet at right angles are **perpendicular** to each other.

- Lines which never meet and are always the same distance apart are **parallel**.

- When two parallel lines are crossed by a **transversal** the following pairs of angles are formed.

Corresponding angles	Alternate angles	Allied angles	
			Arrowheads are used to show that lines are **parallel**.
$a = c$	$b = c$	$b + d = 180°$	

- A **triangle** is a shape made by three straight sides.

- Triangles can be: **acute-angled** (all angles less than 90°),
   obtuse-angled (one angle greater than 90°),
   right-angled (one angle equal to 90°).

- The sum of the angles in a triangle is 180°.
   $a + b + c = 180°$

- The exterior angle is equal to the sum of the two opposite interior angles. $a + b = d$

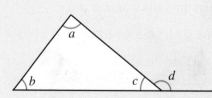

- Types of triangle:

Scalene	Isosceles	Equilateral	
			A **sketch** is used when an accurate drawing is not required. Dashes across lines show sides that are equal in length. Equal angles are marked using arcs.

- A two-dimensional shape has **line symmetry** if the line divides the shape so that one side fits exactly over the other.

- A two-dimensional shape has **rotational symmetry** if it fits into a copy of its outline as it is rotated through 360°.

- A shape is only described as having rotational symmetry if the order of rotational symmetry is 2 or more.

- The number of times a shape fits into its outline in a single turn is the **order of rotational symmetry**.

Order of rotational symmetry 5

- A **quadrilateral** is a shape made by four straight lines.

- The sum of the angles in a quadrilateral is 360°.

- Facts about these special quadrilaterals:

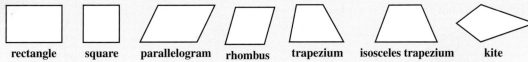

rectangle   square   parallelogram   rhombus   trapezium   isosceles trapezium   kite

Quadrilateral	Sides	Angles	Diagonals	Line symmetry	Order of rotational symmetry
Rectangle	Opposite sides equal and parallel	All 90°	Bisect each other	2	2
Square	4 equal sides, opposite sides parallel	All 90°	Bisect each other at 90°	4	4
Parallelogram	Opposite sides equal and parallel	Opposite angles equal	Bisect each other	0	2
Rhombus	4 equal sides, opposite sides parallel	Opposite angles equal	Bisect each other at 90°	2	2
Trapezium	1 pair of parallel sides				
Isosceles trapezium	1 pair of parallel sides, non-parallel sides equal	2 pairs of equal angles	Equal in length	1	1*
Kite	2 pairs of adjacent sides equal	1 pair of opposite angles equal	One bisects the other at 90°	1	1*

*A shape is only described as having rotational symmetry if the order of rotational symmetry is 2 or more.

- A **polygon** is a many-sided shape made by straight lines.

- A polygon with all sides equal and all angles equal is called a **regular polygon**.

- Shapes you need to know: A 5-sided polygon is called a **pentagon**.
  A 6-sided polygon is called a **hexagon**.
  An 8-sided polygon is called an **octagon**.

- The sum of the exterior angles of any polygon is 360°.

- At each vertex of a polygon: interior angle + exterior angle = 180°

- The sum of the interior angles of an n-sided polygon is given by:
  $$(n - 2) \times 180°$$ n = number of sides.

- For a regular n-sided polygon: exterior angle $= \dfrac{360°}{n}$

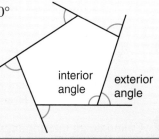

interior angle   exterior angle

- A shape will **tessellate** if it covers a surface without overlapping and leaves no gaps.

Angles and 2-D Shapes

The diagrams in this exercise have not been drawn accurately.

1 Work out the size of the angles marked with letters.
Give a reason for each answer.

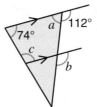

2

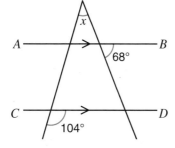

In the diagram, *AB* is parallel to *CD*.
Find the value of *x*.

OCR

3 Find the size of the lettered angles.

(a)  (b) (c)

4 (a) Copy the diagram.
Shade two more squares so that the final diagram has line symmetry only.
(b) Make another copy of the diagram.
Shade two more squares so that the final diagram
has rotational symmetry only.

5

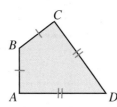

The diagram shows a quadrilateral *ABCD*.
AB = BC and *CD = DA*.
Angle *ADC* = 36° and angle *BCD* = 105°.
Work out the size of angle *ABC*.

6 The diagram shows a regular pentagon, *ABCDE*.
(a) Find the angle *AEB*.
(b) Prove that *BCDE* is a trapezium.

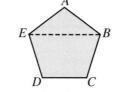

OCR

7

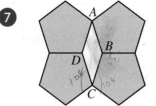

Four regular pentagons are placed together, as shown,
to form a rhombus, *ABCD*.
Calculate the size of
(a) angle *ABC*,
(b) angle *XCY*.

$(10-2)$ $8 \times 180 = \dfrac{1440}{10} = 144$

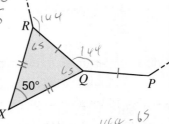

8 *PQ* and *QR* are two sides of a regular 10-sided polygon.
QRX is an isosceles triangle with *RX = XQ*. Angle *QXR* = 50°.
Work out the size of the obtuse angle *PQX*.

$360 - 144 - 65$
$= 79°$
360
$= 281°$

9

ABC is an equilateral triangle.
AC and *CD* are two sides of a regular polygon
and *BC* and *CD* are two sides of an identical polygon.
How many sides has each of these polygons?

10 Calculate an interior angle of a regular 9-sided polygon.

OCR

Circle Properties

What you need to know

- A **circle** is the shape drawn by keeping a pencil the same distance from a fixed point on a piece of paper.

- You should know the meaning of the words shown on the diagrams below.

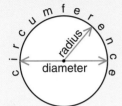 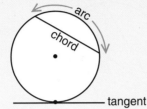 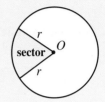

- The vertices of a **cyclic quadrilateral** lie on the circumference of a circle.

- **Circle properties**

  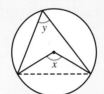 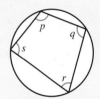

The angle in a semi-circle is a right angle.

Angles in the same segment are equal.

$x = 2y$
The angle at the centre is twice the angle at the circumference.

$p + r = 180°$ and $q + s = 180°$
Opposite angles of a cyclic quadrilateral are supplementary.

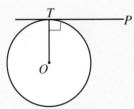 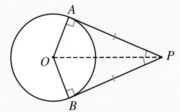 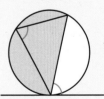

A tangent is perpendicular to the radius at the point of contact.

Tangents drawn to a circle from the same point are equal.

The angle between a tangent and a chord is equal to any angle in the alternate (opposite) segment.

- You should be able to use circle properties to solve problems.

  O is the centre of the circle. Find the marked angles.
  $a = 43°$ (angles in the same segment)
  $b = 2 \times 43°$ ($\angle$ at centre = twice $\angle$ at circum.)
  $b = 86°$
  $c = 180° - 43°$ (opp. $\angle$'s of a cyclic quad)
  $c = 137°$

You should be able to prove that:

- the angle at the centre is twice the angle at the circumference,
- the angle in a semi-circle is a right angle,
- angles in the same segment are equal,
- opposite angles of a cyclic quadrilateral are supplementary,
- the angle between a tangent and a chord is equal to any angle in the alternate segment.

The diagrams in this exercise have not been drawn accurately.

1 O is the centre of the circle.
Work out the size of the lettered angles. Give a reason for each of your answers.

(a) 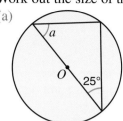   (b) 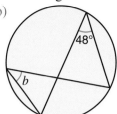   (c) 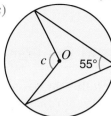   (d)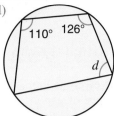

2 O is the centre of the circle.
A, B and C are points on the circle.
AOB is a straight line.

Calculate the sizes of angles x and y.

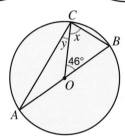

OCR

3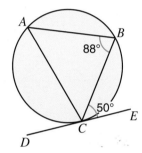

Triangle ABC is inscribed in a circle.
The tangent, DE, touches the circle at C.
Angle $ABC = 88°$.   Angle $BCE = 50°$.

(a)   Explain how you know that AC is **not** a diameter of the circle.
(b)   Calculate the size of angle ACB. Explain your answer.   OCR

4 AXB is a tangent to the circle, centre O.

Find the size of the angles marked a, b and c.

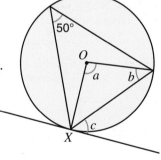

5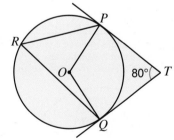

PT and QT are tangents from the point T to the circle, centre O.
Angle $PTQ = 80°$.

Calculate angle PRQ.
Give a reason for each step in your calculation.   OCR

6 $ABCD$ is a cyclic quadrilateral. AD is parallel to BC.
$\angle ABD = 32°$ and $\angle CBD = 53°$.

Find   (a)   angle ADB,   (b)   angle ACD,
(c)   angle ADC,   (d)   angle BAD.

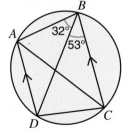

7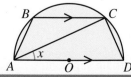

The diagram shows a semi-circle, centre O.
Angle $CAD = x°$ and BC is parallel to AD.

Find, in terms of x, angle ABC.

Perimeters and Areas

What you need to know

- **Perimeter** is the distance round the outside of a shape.
- **Area** is the amount of surface covered by a shape.
- You should be able to use these formulae to find areas.

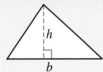 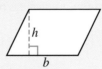 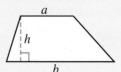

Triangle: $A = \frac{1}{2} \times b \times h$ **Rectangle:** $A = lb$ **Parallelogram:** $A = bh$ **Trapezium:** $A = \frac{1}{2}(a + b)h$

Eg 1 Calculate the area of this triangle.

$A = \frac{1}{2} \times b \times h$
$A = \frac{1}{2} \times 6 \times 4 \, \text{cm}^2$
$A = 12 \, \text{cm}^2$

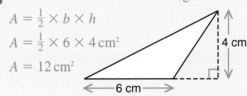

Eg 2 Find the area of this trapezium.

$A = \frac{1}{2}(a + b)h$
$A = \frac{1}{2}(6 + 9)5$
$A = \frac{1}{2} \times 15 \times 5$
$A = 37.5 \, \text{cm}^2$

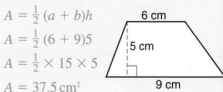

- You should be able to calculate **lengths** and **areas** associated with **circles**.

> **Circumference** of a circle is given by: $C = \pi d$ or $C = 2\pi r$
>
> **Area** of a circle is given by: $A = \pi r^2$
>
> The **lengths of arcs** and the **areas of sectors** are proportional to the angle at the centre of the circle.
>
> For a sector with angle $a°$
>
> **Length of arc** $= \frac{a}{360} \times \pi d$
>
> **Area of sector** $= \frac{a}{360} \times \pi r^2$

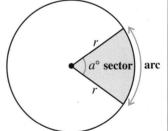

Take π to be 3.14 or use the π key on your calculator.

Eg 3 Find the circumference of a circle with radius 9 cm.
Give your answer to 1 d.p.

$C = 2 \times \pi \times r$
$C = 2 \times \pi \times 9$
$C = 56.548...$
$C = 56.5 \, \text{cm}$, correct to 1 d.p.

Eg 4 Find the area of a circle with radius 6 cm.
Give your answer to 3 sig. figs.

$A = \pi \times r^2$
$A = \pi \times 6 \times 6$
$A = 113.097...$
$A = 113 \, \text{cm}^2$, correct to 3 sig. figs.

Eg 5 A circle has a circumference of 25.2 cm. Find the diameter of the circle.

$C = \pi d$, so, $d = \frac{C}{\pi}$
$d = \frac{25.2}{\pi}$
$d = 8.021...$
$d = 8.0 \, \text{cm}$, correct to 1 d.p.

Eg 6 A circle has an area of 154 cm². Find the radius of the circle.

$A = \pi r^2$, so, $r^2 = \frac{A}{\pi}$
$r^2 = \frac{154}{\pi} = 49.019...$
$r = \sqrt{49.019...} = 7.001...$
$r = 7 \, \text{cm}$, to the nearest cm.

Eg 7 *OAB* is a sector of a circle of radius 7.2 cm.   Angle *AOB* = 50°.
Calculate   (a)   the length of arc *AB*,
                   (b)   the area of sector *AOB*.

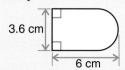

(a)   Length of arc $= \frac{a}{360} \times \pi d = \frac{50}{360} \times \pi \times 14.4$

$= 6.2831\ldots = 6.28$ cm, correct to 3 s.f.

(b)   Area of sector $= \frac{a}{360} \times \pi r^2 = \frac{50}{360} \times \pi \times 7.2^2$

$= 22.619\ldots = 22.6$ cm², correct to 3 s.f.

● Shapes formed by joining different shapes together are called **compound shapes**.
To find the area of a compound shape we must first divide the shape up into rectangles,
triangles, circles, etc., and find the area of each part.

Eg 8   Find the area of this metal plate.

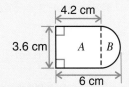

The plate can be divided into a rectangle, *A*, and a semi-circle, *B*.
Area *A* $= 3.6 \times 4.2 = 15.12$ cm²
Area *B* $= \frac{1}{2} \times \pi \times 1.8^2 = 5.089\ldots$ cm²
Total area $= 15.12 + 5.089\ldots = 20.2$ cm², correct to 3 s.f.

Exercise 25

Take π to be 3.14 or use the π key on your calculator.

1   Calculate the area of this shape.

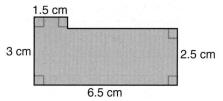

2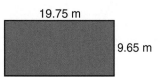

The diagram shows a rectangular garden.
Selina wants to estimate the area of the garden.
(a)   Write down a calculation she could do in her head
       to estimate the area of the garden.
(b)   Is your estimate bigger or smaller than the exact area?
       Explain how you decide.   OCR

3   Calculate the area of triangle *PQR*.

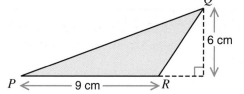

4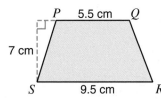

The diagram shows a trapezium, *PQRS*.
Calculate the area of the trapezium.

5   This design is made with three semi-circles, each of diameter 8 cm.
Find the perimeter of the design.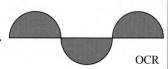

OCR

6   A rectangular carpet is twice as long as it is wide. The carpet covers an area of 24.5 m².
Calculate the length of the carpet.

7 A photo frame is a square of side 20 cm.
It has a circular glass section and the rest is brass.
Work out the area of the brass part of the photo frame.

OCR

8 The diagram shows the plan of a swimming pool.
The arc QR is a semi-circle.
$PS = 12$ m and $PQ = RS = 20$ m.
Calculate the area of the surface of the pool.

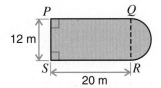

9 The logo for a football team is a white circle with a blue design inside.
The team paint their logo on the pitch.
The circle has a radius of 5 m.
The blue area covers 35% of the circle.
Find the area painted blue.

OCR

10 A toy is made by cutting a circle, radius 6 cm,
out of a circular piece of plastic, radius 9 cm.
Calculate the shaded area.
Give your answer in terms of π, as simply as possible.

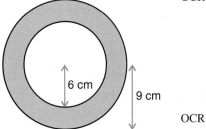

OCR

11 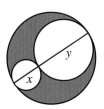 Three circles overlap, as shown.
The largest circle has a diameter of 12 cm.
The ratio of the diameters $x : y$ is 1 : 2.
Calculate the shaded area.
Give your answer in terms of π.

12 A circle has an area of 100 cm².
Calculate the circumference of the circle.
Give your answer correct to three significant figures.

13 Alfie says,   *"A semi-circle with a radius of 10 cm has a larger area than a whole circle with half the radius."*
Is he correct?
You **must** show working to justify your answer.

14 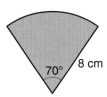 The diagram shows a sector of a circle of radius 8 cm.
Calculate the perimeter of the sector.

15 A wiper blade on a windscreen cleans the area shown.
Calculate the area of windscreen cleaned by the wiper.
Give your answer in terms of π.

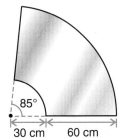

16 A circle, of radius 5.6 cm, is cut into two sectors.
The areas of the sectors are in the ratio 2 : 3.
Calculate the area and perimeter of the smaller sector.
Give your answer correct to a suitable degree of accuracy.

17 The area of a sector of a circle is 32 cm². The diameter of the circle is 13 cm.
Calculate the perimeter of the sector.

Perimeters and Areas

Maps, Loci and Constructions

What you need to know

- **Compass points** and **three-figure bearings** are used to describe direction.
- A **bearing** is an angle measured from the North line in a clockwise direction.
- A bearing can be any angle from 0° to 360° and is written as a three-figure number.
- To find a bearing: measure angle a to find the bearing of Y from X,
  measure angle b to find the bearing of X from Y.

- **Scales**

  The distances between points on a map are all drawn to the same scale.
  There are two ways to describe a scale.
  1. A scale of 1 cm to 10 km means that a distance of 1 cm on the map represents an actual distance of 10 km.
  2. A scale of 1 : 10 000 means that all distances measured on the map have to be multiplied by 10 000 to find the real distance.

- The path of a point which moves according to a rule is called a **locus**.
- The word **loci** is used when we talk about more than one locus.
- You should be able to draw the locus of a point which moves according to a given rule.

  Eg 1 A ball is rolled along this zig-zag.
  Draw the locus of P, the centre of the ball, as it is rolled along.

Using a ruler and compasses you should be able to:
- Construct the **perpendicular from a point to a line**.
- Construct the **perpendicular from a point on a line**.
- Construct the **perpendicular bisector of a line**.

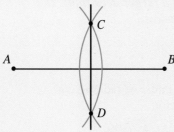

Points on the line CD are **equidistant** from the points A and B.

- Construct the **bisector of an angle**.

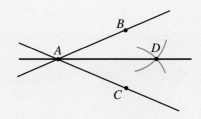

Points on the line AD are **equidistant** from the lines AB and AC.

- You should be able to solve loci problems which involve using these constructions.

  Eg 2 P is a point inside triangle ABC such that:
  (i) P is equidistant from points A and B,
  (ii) P is equidistant from lines AB and BC.
  Find the position of P.

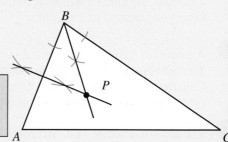

  > To find point P:
  > (i)   construct the perpendicular bisector of line AB,
  > (ii) construct the bisector of angle ABC.

  P is at the point where these lines intersect.

1 The diagram shows a sketch of the course to be used for a running event.

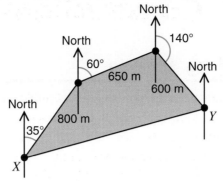

(a) Draw an accurate plan of the course, using a scale of 1 cm to represent 100 m.
(b) Use your plan to find (i) the bearing of X from Y,
(ii) the distance XY in metres.

2 The ball is rolled along the zig-zag.
Copy the diagram and draw the locus of the centre of the ball as it is rolled from X to Y.

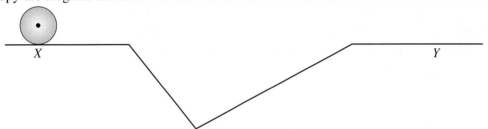

3 **In this question, you should use only ruler and compasses.**
You must show your construction lines.
(a) Construct an equilateral triangle with sides of length 7 cm.
(b) Construct the angle bisector of one of the angles of your triangle.   OCR

4 The diagram shows the scale drawing of a garden, *ABCD*.

The scale is **1 cm to 2 m**.

Copy the diagram.
(a) Construct the bisector of angle *A*.
Show all your construction lines.
(b) A tree is to be planted in the garden.
It must be nearer to *AD* than *AB* and at least 8 m from *C*.
Shade the region in which the tree could be planted.   OCR

5 (a) Construct a kite *PQRS* in which   *PQ = PS = 7* cm,   *QR = RS = 5* cm
and the diagonal   *QS = 6* cm.
X is a point inside the kite such that: (i)   *X* is equidistant from *P* and *Q*,
(ii) *X* is equidistant from sides *PQ* and *PS*.
(b) By constructing the loci for (i) and (ii) find the position of *X*.
(c) Measure the distance *PX*.

Transformations

What you need to know

- The movement of a shape from one position to another is called a **transformation**.

- **Single transformations** can be described in terms of a reflection, a rotation, a translation or an enlargement.

- **Reflection**: The image of the shape is the same distance from the mirror line as the original.

- **Rotation**: All points are turned through the same angle about the same point, called a centre of rotation.

- **Translation**: All points are moved the same distance in the same direction without turning.

- **Enlargement**: All lengths are multiplied by a scale factor.

$$\text{Scale factor} = \frac{\text{new length}}{\text{original length}}$$ | New length = scale factor × original length |

The size of the original shape is:
  increased by using a scale factor greater than 1,
  reduced by using a scale factor which is a fraction, i.e. between 0 and 1.
When a shape is enlarged using a **negative scale factor** the image is **inverted**.

- You should be able to draw the transformation of a shape.

  Eg 1 Draw the image of triangle P after it has been translated with vector $\begin{pmatrix} -3 \\ 2 \end{pmatrix}$.

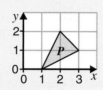

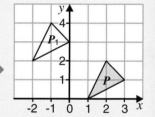

- You should be able to fully describe transformations.

Transformation	Image same shape and size?	Details needed to describe the transformation
Reflection	Yes	Mirror line, sometimes given as an equation.
Rotation	Yes	Centre of rotation, amount of turn, direction of turn.
Translation	Yes	Horizontal movement and vertical movement. Vector: top number = horizontal movement, bottom number = vertical movement.
Enlargement	No	Centre of enlargement, scale factor.

Eg 2 Describe the single transformation which maps
  (a) A onto B,
  (b) A onto C,
  (c) A onto D,
  (d) D onto E,
  (e) E onto F.

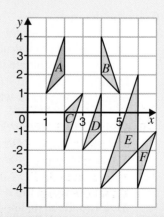

  (a) **Reflection** in the line $x = 3$.
  (b) **Rotation** of $180°$ about $(2, 1)$.
  (c) **Translation** with vector $\begin{pmatrix} 2 \\ -3 \end{pmatrix}$.
  (d) **Enlargement** scale factor 2, centre $(2, 0)$.
  (e) **Enlargement** scale factor $-\frac{1}{2}$, centre $(6, -2)$.

1. The diagram shows the positions of kites *P*, *Q*, *R* and *S*.

   (a) (i) *P* is mapped onto *Q* by a reflection. What is the equation of the line of reflection?
       (ii) *P* is mapped onto *R* by a translation. What is the vector of the translation?
       (iii) *P* is mapped onto *S* by an enlargement. What is the centre and scale factor of the enlargement?

   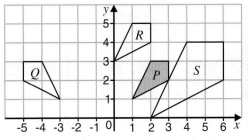

   (b) *P* is mapped onto *T* by a rotation through $90°$ clockwise about $(1, -2)$. On squared paper, copy *P* and draw the position of *T*.

2. In each diagram, *A* is mapped onto *B* by a single transformation. Describe each transformation.

   (a) 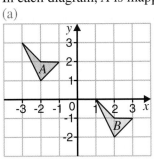 (b) 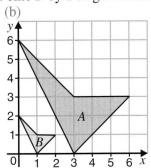 (c)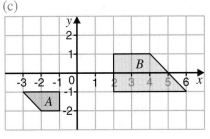

3. (a) Describe fully the single transformation that maps
       (i) *A* onto *B*,
       (ii) *A* onto *C*.

   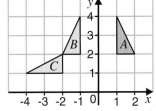

   (b) 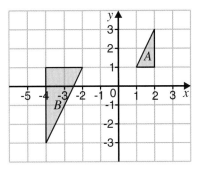 *Q* is reflected in $x = 4$ and then in $y = 1$. Describe fully the single transformation that is equivalent to these two transformations.

   OCR

4. Describe fully the **single** transformation that maps triangle *A* onto triangle *B*.

   OCR

5. Triangle *PQR* has vertices $P(2, -3)$, $Q(-2, -5)$, $R(-4, -3)$.
   On squared paper, draw and label triangle *PQR*.

   (a) Enlarge triangle *PQR* by scale factor $\frac{1}{2}$ from the centre of enlargement $(4, -1)$. Label the image *A*.
   (b) Rotate triangle *PQR* through $180°$ about the point $(-2, -1)$. Label the image *B*.
   (c) Describe fully the single transformation which maps triangle *A* onto triangle *B*.

Pythagoras' Theorem

What you need to know

- The longest side in a right-angled triangle is called the **hypotenuse**.

- The **Theorem of Pythagoras** states:
  "In any right-angled triangle the square on the hypotenuse is equal to the sum of the squares on the other two sides."
  $$a^2 = b^2 + c^2$$

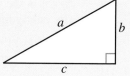

- When we know the lengths of two sides of a right-angled triangle, we can use the Theorem of Pythagoras to find the length of the third side.

$a^2 = b^2 + c^2$
Rearranging gives: $b^2 = a^2 - c^2$
$c^2 = a^2 - b^2$

Eg 1 Calculate the length of side a.

Eg 2 Calculate the length of side b.

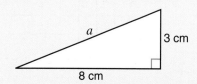

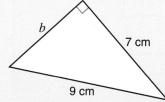

$a^2 = b^2 + c^2$

$a^2 = 8^2 + 3^2$

$a^2 = 64 + 9 = 73$

$a = \sqrt{73} = 8.544\ldots$

$a = 8.5\,\text{cm}$, correct to 1 d.p.

$b^2 = a^2 - c^2$

$b^2 = 9^2 - 7^2$

$b^2 = 81 - 49 = 32$

$b = \sqrt{32} = 5.656\ldots$

$b = 5.7\,\text{cm}$, correct to 1 d.p.

Exercise 28   Do not use a calculator for questions 1 and 2.

1 ABC is a right-angled triangle.
$AB = 5\,\text{cm}$ and $AC = 12\,\text{cm}$.
Calculate the length of BC.

2

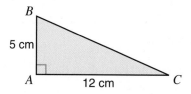

The diagram shows the cross-section of the roof of a house.
The width of the house, PR, is $10\,\text{m}$.
$QR = 6\,\text{m}$ and angle $PQR = 90°$.
Calculate the length of PQ.

3 The diagram shows a rectangular sheet of paper.
The paper is $20\,\text{cm}$ wide and the diagonal, d, is $35\,\text{cm}$.

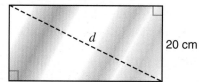

Calculate the length of the sheet of paper.

4 The diagram shows the points $A(1, 2)$ and $B(5, 8)$.

    (a) Find the coordinates of the midpoint of AB.

    (b) Calculate the length of the line AB.

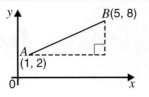

OCR

5 Calculate the length of the line joining the points $A(-2, -3)$ and $B(6, 1)$.

6

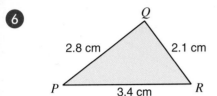

Is PQR: an acute-angled triangle,
an obtuse-angled triangle,
or a right-angled triangle?

Show your calculations and state your conclusions.

7 A football pitch measures 100 m by 72 m.

Mike walks along the edge of the pitch from A to B.
Alan walks diagonally across the pitch from A to B.

Calculate how much further Mike walks than Alan.

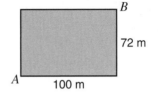

OCR

8

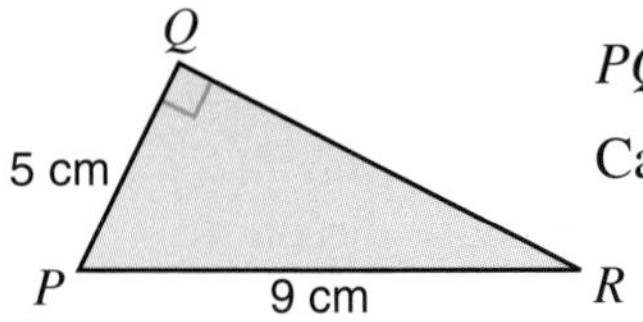

PQR is a right-angled triangle. $PQ = 5$ cm and $PR = 9$ cm.

Calculate the length of QR and, hence, find the area of triangle PQR.

9 The square, $ABCD$, has an area of 50 cm^2.

Calculate the length of the diagonal, AC.

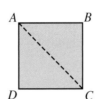

10

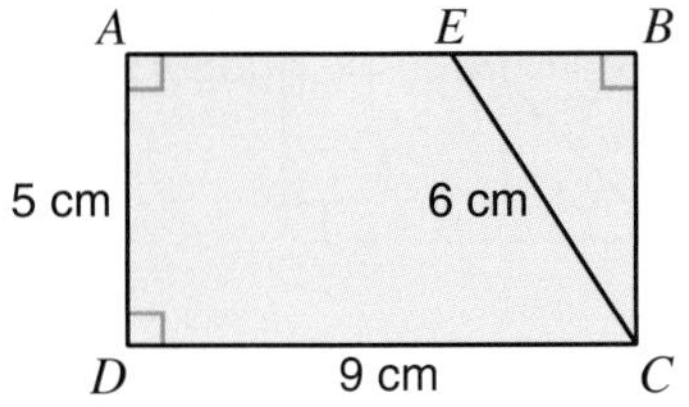

$ABCD$ is a rectangle.
$AD = 5$ cm, $DC = 9$ cm and $EC = 6$ cm.

Calculate the length of AE, correct to one decimal place.

11 A cuboid has dimensions 20 cm by 10 cm by 5 cm.

Calculate the length of the diagonal AB.
Give your answer to a suitable degree of accuracy.

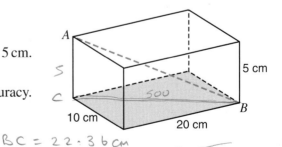

$BC = 22 \cdot 36$ cm

$AB^2 \sqrt{525} = 22.91$ cm.

12

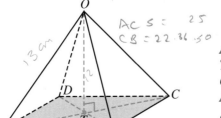

$AC s = 25$
$CB = 22.36 \cdot 50$

$ABCDO$ is a square-based right pyramid.
T is the centre of the square base.
$OT = 12$ cm.
$AO = BO = CO = DO = 13$ cm.

Show that $BC = \sqrt{50}$ cm.

OCR

What you need to know

- **Trigonometry** is used to find the lengths of sides and the sizes of angles in right-angled triangles.

- You must learn the **sine**, **cosine** and **tangent** ratios.

$$\sin a = \frac{\text{opposite}}{\text{hypotenuse}} \quad \cos a = \frac{\text{adjacent}}{\text{hypotenuse}} \quad \tan a = \frac{\text{opposite}}{\text{adjacent}}$$

- Each ratio links the size of an angle with the lengths of two sides. If we are given the values for two of these we can find the value of the third.

- When we look **up** from the horizontal the angle we turn through is called the **angle of elevation**.

- When we look **down** from the horizontal the angle we turn through is called the **angle of depression**.

- Bearings are used to describe the direction in which you must travel to get from one place to another. They are measured from the North line in a clockwise direction. A bearing can be any angle from 0° to 360° and is written as a three-figure number.

- You should be able to use trigonometry to find the lengths of sides and the sizes of angles when solving problems involving right-angled triangles.

| Eg 1 | Find the length, d. |

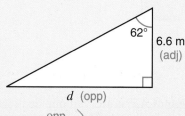

$$\tan a = \frac{\text{opp}}{\text{adj}}$$
$$\tan 62° = \frac{d}{6.6}$$
$$d = 6.6 \times \tan 62°$$
$$d = 12.412\ldots$$
$$d = 12.4 \text{ m, correct to 3 s.f.}$$

| Eg 2 | Find the size of angle a. |

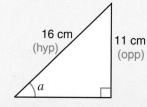

$$\sin a = \frac{\text{opp}}{\text{hyp}}$$
$$\sin a° = \frac{11}{16}$$
$$a = \sin^{-1} \frac{11}{16}$$
$$a = 43.432\ldots$$
$$a = 43.4°, \text{ correct to 1 d.p.}$$

- When working in three dimensions the first task is to identify the length, or angle, that you are trying to find.
  The length, or angle, will always form part of a triangle together with either:
  two other sides of known length, or
  one side of known length and an angle of known size.
  Sometimes, more than one triangle is needed to solve a problem.

- A straight line meets a plane at a **point**.
  The angle *XPT* is the **angle between the line and the plane**.
  The line *XT* is perpendicular to the plane.

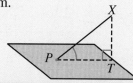

Exercise 29   Do not use a calculator for question 1.

1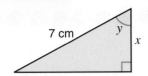
In the right-angled triangle shown:
$\sin y = 0.8$ and $\cos y = 0.6$
Find the value of x.

2 The diagram shows two positions of an advertising balloon.
The balloon is fixed to the ground by a straight cable
of length 21 metres.

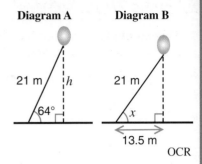

(a) Calculate the vertical height, h, of the balloon
above the ground in **Diagram A**.
(b) Calculate the angle, x, which the cable makes with
the horizontal ground for the balloon in **Diagram B**.

OCR

3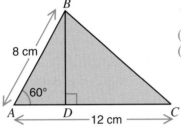

(a) Calculate the area of the triangle ABC.
(b) Calculate the length DC.

OCR

4 A ladder is placed against a vertical wall with its foot on horizontal ground.
The ladder is 4.3 m long and reaches 3.9 m up the wall.
For safety reasons, the ladder should make an
angle of 70° with the ground.

How far should the foot of the ladder be moved
towards the wall for safety?

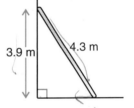

OCR

5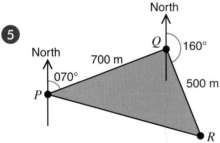
The diagram shows the path of a jet-ski from P to Q to R.

Q is 700 m from P on a bearing of 070°.
R is 500 m from Q on a bearing of 160°.

Calculate the bearing of P from R.

6 $XABCD$ is a pyramid on a square base of side 8 cm.
$XA = XB = XC = XD = 9$ cm.

(a) Calculate XO, the perpendicular height of the pyramid.
(b) Find the angle between XC and the base.

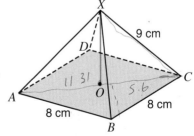

7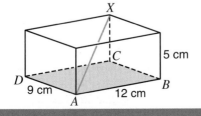
A cuboid has dimensions 12 cm by 9 cm by 5 cm.

Calculate the angle between the diagonal XA and the
base, $ABCD$.

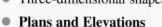

- **You should be able to:**
- find the number of **faces**, **edges** and **vertices** of a 3-D shape,
- draw the **net** of a 3-D shape,
- use **isometric** paper to make a 2-D drawing of a 3-D shape.
- A **plane of symmetry** slices through a 3-D shape so that one half is the mirror image of the other half.
- Three-dimensional shapes can have **axes of symmetry**.
- **Plans and Elevations**
  The view of a 3-D shape looking from above is called a **plan**.
  The view of a 3-D shape from the front or sides is called an **elevation**.

  Eg 1 Draw diagrams to show the plan and elevation from **X**, for this 3-dimensional shape.

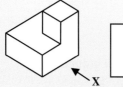

  X **plan** **elevation X**

  Dotted lines are used to show hidden edges.

- **Volume** is the amount of space occupied by a 3-D shape.
- The formula for the volume of a **cuboid** is:
  Volume = length × breadth × height
  $V = l \times b \times h$

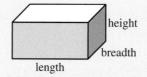

  height
  breadth
  length

- Volume of a **cube** is: $V = l^3$
- To find the **surface area** of a cuboid, find the areas of the 6 rectangular faces and add the answers together.

- **Prisms**
  If you make a cut at right angles to the length of a prism you will always get the same cross-section.

  Triangular prism
  cross-section
  length

- Volume of a prism = area of cross-section × length

  Eg 2 Calculate the volume of this prism.   ‹ ½(a+b)h
  The cross-section of this prism is a trapezium.

  Area of cross-section = $\frac{1}{2}$ (5 + 3) × 2.5
  $\qquad = 4 \times 2.5$
  $\qquad = 10\,\text{cm}^2$
  Volume of prism = area of cross-section × length
  $\qquad = 10 \times 12$
  $\qquad = 120\,\text{cm}^3$

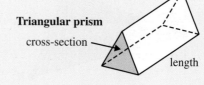

  5 cm   3 cm
  2.5 cm   12 cm

- A **cylinder** is a prism.
  Volume of a cylinder is: Volume = $\pi \times r^2 \times h$
  Surface area of a cylinder is: Surface area = $2\pi r^2 + 2\pi rh$

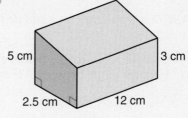

  r
  h

Eg 3 A cylinder has a radius of 4 cm and a height of 6 cm.
Calculate (a) the volume and (b) the surface area of the cylinder.

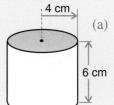

(a) $V = \pi r^2 h$
$= \pi \times 4 \times 4 \times 6$
$= 301.592...$
$= 302$ cm³,
correct to 3 s.f.

(b) Surface area $= 2\pi r^2 + 2\pi rh$
$= 2 \times \pi \times 4 \times 4 + 2 \times \pi \times 4 \times 6$
$= 100.53... + 150.796...$
$= 251$ cm²,
correct to 3 s.f.

● These formulae are used in calculations involving **cones**, **pyramids** and **spheres**.

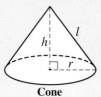

Cone

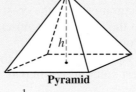

Pyramid

Sphere

$V = \frac{1}{3} \times$ base area $\times$ height
$V = \frac{1}{3}\pi r^2 h$
Curved surface area $= \pi rl$

$V = \frac{1}{3} \times$ base area $\times$ height

Volume $= \frac{4}{3}\pi r^3$
Surface area $= 4\pi r^2$

Eg 4 A cone is 6.4 cm high and has a
radius of 4.8 cm.
Calculate the curved surface area
of the cone.

Slant height, $l = \sqrt{6.4^2 + 4.8^2}$
$= \sqrt{64} = 8$ cm

Curved surface area is given by:
$\pi rl = \pi \times 4.8 \times 8 = 120.637...$
$= 120.6$ cm², correct to 1 d.p.

Eg 5 A steel ball has a radius of 4 cm.
Calculate (a) the volume,
(b) the surface area of the ball.

(a) Volume $= \frac{4}{3}\pi r^3 = \frac{4}{3} \times \pi \times 4^3$
$= 268.082...$
$= 268$ cm³, correct to 3 s.f.

(b) Surface area $= 4\pi r^2 = 4 \times \pi \times 4^2$
$= 201.061...$
$= 201$ cm², correct to 3 s.f.

● A **frustum of a cone** is formed by removing the
top of a cone with a cut parallel to its circular base.

Exercise 30   Do not use a calculator for questions 1 to 5.

1 The diagram shows a square-based pyramid.
(a) How many planes of symmetry has the pyramid?
(b) How many axes of symmetry has the pyramid?

2

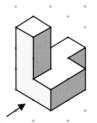

The diagram shows a solid drawn on isometric paper.
(a) Draw the plan of the solid.
(b) Draw the elevation of the solid from the direction
shown by the arrow.

3 (a) Which of these cuboids has the larger volume?
Show all your working.
(b) Which cuboid has the larger surface area?

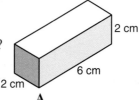

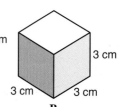

A   **B**

4 A cuboid has a volume of 100 cm³. The cuboid is 8 cm long and 5 cm wide.
Calculate the surface area of the cuboid.

5 A cylinder has a radius of 6 cm and a height of 5 cm.
Calculate the volume of the cylinder.
Give your answer in terms of π.

6 The diagram shows a grit bin.
The bin is a prism.
Calculate the capacity of the bin.

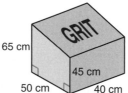

65 cm
45 cm
50 cm
40 cm

OCR

7

12 cm

(a) The diagram shows the cross-section of a water trough.
It is in the shape of a semi-circle with radius 12 cm.
The trough is 84 m long.
What volume of water can the trough hold?
(b) Convert your answer in part (a) to litres.

OCR

8 A kitchen waste bin is a prism.
The cross-section is a rectangle 30 cm wide and 50 cm high,
topped by a semi-circle of radius 15 cm. The bin has a square base.
(a) Draw the plan and the front elevation viewed from F.
Use a scale of 1 cm to 10 cm.
(b) Calculate the total volume of the waste bin.

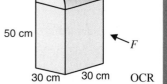

50 cm
F
30 cm   30 cm   OCR

9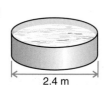

2.4 m

A cylindrical water tank has radius 40 cm and height 90 cm.
(a) Calculate the total surface area of the tank.

A full tank of water is used to fill a paddling pool.
(b) The paddling pool is a cylinder with diameter 2.4 metres.
Calculate the depth of water in the pool.

10 The diagram represents the glass cover placed over an anniversary clock.
The cover is formed by joining a cylindrical tube to a hemispherical shell.
The radius of both the cylinder and hemisphere is 5.8 cm.
The total height of the cover is 20.5 cm.
Calculate the surface area of the cover.

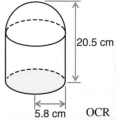

20.5 cm

5.8 cm   OCR

11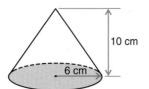

10 cm
6 cm

A cone is 10 cm high and has a base radius of 6 cm.
(a) Calculate the curved surface area of the cone.

The top of the cone is cut off to leave a frustum 8 cm high.
(b) Calculate the volume of the frustum.

12 Rachel buys a ball in a box. The ball touches each side of the box.
The box is a cube with sides of length 20 cm.
(a) Calculate the difference between the volume of the box and
the volume of the ball.
(b) Calculate the difference between the surface area of the box
and the surface area of the ball.

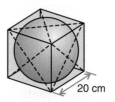

20 cm

13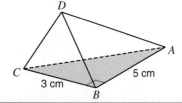

D
A
C
3 cm
5 cm
B

The diagram shows a triangular pyramid.
Angle $ABC = 90°$, $AB = 5$ cm and $BC = 3$ cm.
The volume of the pyramid is 28 cm³.
Calculate the height of the pyramid.

Understanding and Using Measures

What you need to know

- The common units — both **metric** and **imperial** — used to measure **length**, **mass** and **capacity**.

- How to convert from one unit to another. This includes knowing the connection between one metric unit and another and the approximate equivalents between metric and imperial units.

Metric Units	Imperial Units	Conversions
Length 1 kilometre (km) = 1000 metres (m) 1 m = 100 centimetres (cm) 1 cm = 10 millimetres (mm) **Mass** 1 tonne (t) = 1000 kilograms (kg) 1 kg = 1000 grams (g) **Capacity and volume** 1 litre = 1000 millilitres (ml) $1\,cm^3 = 1\,ml$	**Length** 1 foot = 12 inches 1 yard = 3 feet **Mass** 1 pound = 16 ounces 14 pounds = 1 stone **Capacity and volume** 1 gallon = 8 pints	**Length** 5 miles is about 8 km 1 inch is about 2.5 cm 1 foot is about 30 cm **Mass** 1 kg is about 2.2 pounds **Capacity and volume** 1 litre is about 1.75 pints 1 gallon is about 4.5 litres

- How to change between units of area. For example $1\,m^2 = 10\,000\,cm^2$.

- How to change between units of volume. For example $1\,m^3 = 1\,000\,000\,cm^3$.

- You should be able to recognise limitations on the accuracy of measurements.
  A **discrete measure** can only take a particular value and a **continuous measure** lies within a range of possible values which depends upon the degree of accuracy of the measurement.

> If a **continuous measure**, c, is recorded to the nearest x, then the limits of the possible values of c can be written as $c \pm \frac{1}{2}x$.

Eg 1 A log is 12 m in length. The length is correct to the nearest metre.
What is the minimum length of the log?   Minimum length = 12 − 0.5 = 11.5 m

Eg 2 A road is 400 m long, to the nearest 10 m.
Between what lengths is the actual length of the road?
Actual length = 400 m ± 5 m   395 m ⩽ actual length < 405 m

Eg 3 A punnet of strawberries weighs 2.4 kg, correct to the nearest 100 g.
Between what limits must the weight of the strawberries lie?
Actual weight = 2.4 kg ± 0.05 kg
Lower limit = 2.35 kg
Upper limit = 2.45 kg
So, 2.35 kg ⩽ actual weight < 2.45 kg.

- By analysing the **dimensions** of a formula it is possible to decide whether a given formula represents a **length** (dimension 1), an **area** (dimension 2) or a **volume** (dimension 3).

Eg 4 p, q, r and s represent lengths.
By using dimensions, decide whether the expression $pq + qr + rs$
could represent a perimeter, an area or a volume.
Writing $pq + qr + rs$ using dimensions:
$$L \times L + L \times L + L \times L = L^2 + L^2 + L^2 = 3L^2$$
So, $pq + qr + rs$ has dimension 2 and could represent an area.

1 On a map the distance between two hospitals is 14.5 cm.
The map has been drawn to a scale of 1 to 250 000.
Calculate the actual distance between the hospitals in kilometres.

2 Debbie is 5 feet 4 inches tall and weighs 9 stone 2 lb. Joyce is 155 cm tall and weighs 60 kg.
Who is taller? Who is heavier? You must show your working.

3 Last year Felicity drove 2760 miles on business.
Her car does 38 miles per gallon.
Petrol costs 89 pence per litre.
She is given a car allowance of 25 pence per kilometre.
How much of her car allowance is left after paying for her petrol?
Give your answer to the nearest £.

4 (a) A beach towel is rectangular in shape and measures 1.8 m by 90 cm.
Calculate the area of the towel in square metres.
(b) Change 0.2 m³ to cm³.

5 A bag of carrots weighs 2.5 kg, correct to the nearest 100 g.
What is the minimum weight of the bag of carrots?

6 Pete cycles at 15 miles per hour.
What is his speed in kilometres per hour?

7 In these expressions, a, b and c represent lengths.
$$\pi(a + b) \qquad a^2 + ab + abc \qquad \frac{\pi a^2}{4} + \frac{\pi ac}{2} \qquad \pi a^2(b + c)$$
Which one of these expressions could represent an area? Show how you decide.   OCR

8 The length and width of a rectangular piece of paper were measured to the nearest centimetre.
The measurements recorded were 22 cm and 13 cm.
Find the smallest possible value of the perimeter of the piece of paper.   OCR

9 A lift can safely carry a load of 500 kg to the nearest 20 kg.
Six people weigh 50 kg, 70 kg, 100 kg, 95 kg, 80 kg and 85 kg, all measured to the nearest 5 kg.
Is it safe for them all to use the lift at the same time?
You must show the calculations on which you base your answer.   OCR

10 Mike has measured his rectangular lawn.
The length is 13 metres and the width is 7 metres.
Both measurements are correct to the nearest metre.
Calculate the upper bound for the area of the lawn.   OCR

11 The measurements of a rectangular ticket are given as 5 cm by 3 cm, correct to the nearest centimetre.
(a) Between what limits must the width of the ticket lie?
(b) Between what limits must the area of the ticket lie?
(c) The area of the ticket is given as $(15 \pm x)$ cm².
Suggest a suitable value for x.

12 Michael rides his bicycle to work.
The diameter of each wheel is 65 cm, correct to the nearest centimetre.
The distance he cycles to work is 2.4 km, correct to one decimal place.
Calculate the least number of turns each wheel makes when Michael cycles to work.

13 $x = 6$,   correct to 1 significant figure.
$y = 0.3$,   correct to 1 decimal place.
Calculate the smallest possible value of $\frac{x + y}{y}$.

Congruent Triangles and Similar Figures

What you need to know

- When two shapes are the same shape and size they are said to be **congruent**.

- There are four ways to show that a pair of triangles are congruent.

SSS	3 corresponding sides.	**ASA**	2 angles and a corresponding side.
SAS	2 sides and the included angle.	**RHS**	Right angle, hypotenuse and one other side.

Eg 1   Show that triangles ABC and XYZ are congruent.

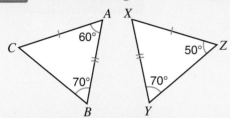

$AC = XZ$ (given)
$AB = XY$ (given)
$\angle BAC = \angle YXZ = 60°$ (sum of angles in $\Delta = 180°$)

So, triangles ABC and XYZ are congruent (SAS).

- When two figures are **similar**:
  their **shapes** are the same, their **angles** are the same,
  corresponding **lengths** are in the same ratio,
  this ratio is the **scale factor** of the enlargement.

$$\text{Scale factor} = \frac{\text{new length}}{\text{original length}}$$

- For **similar triangles**:
  corresponding lengths are opposite equal angles,
  the scale factor is the ratio of the
  corresponding sides.

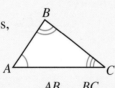

$$\frac{AB}{PQ} = \frac{BC}{QR} = \frac{CA}{RP} = \text{scale factor}$$

- You should be able to find corresponding lengths in similar triangles.

Eg 2   These two triangles are similar.
Find the lengths of the sides marked x and y.

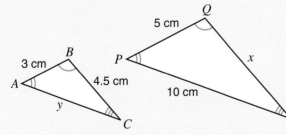

AB and PQ are corresponding sides.
Scale factor $= \dfrac{PQ}{AB} = \dfrac{5}{3}$

$x = 4.5 \times \dfrac{5}{3} = 7.5\,\text{cm}$

$y = 10 \div \dfrac{5}{3} = 6\,\text{cm}$

- You should be able to find corresponding lengths, areas and volumes in similar figures.

When the **length** scale factor $= k$,   the **area** scale factor $= k^2$,   the **volume** scale factor $= k^3$.

Eg 3   Two fish tanks are similar. The smaller tank is 12 cm high and holds 4 litres of water.
The larger tank is 18 cm high. How many litres of water does it hold?

Ratio of heights is $12 : 18 = 2 : 3$.
Ratio of volumes is $2^3 : 3^3 = 8 : 27$.

Water in larger tank $= 4 \times \dfrac{27}{8} = 13.5$ litres

To find the ratio of volumes,
cube the ratio of lengths.

79

The diagrams in this exercise have not been drawn accurately.

1 Which two of these triangles are congruent to each other?
   Give a reason for your answer.

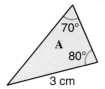 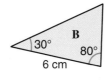 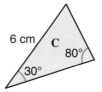

2 The diagram shows rectangles **A**, **B** and **C**.

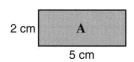 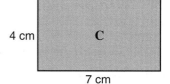

   (a) Explain why rectangles **A** and **C** are **not** similar.
   (b) Rectangles **A** and **B** are similar.
        Work out the length of rectangle **B**.

3 *ABC* and *PQR* are similar triangles.

   Find the length marked (a) x
                           (b) y

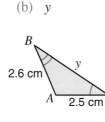 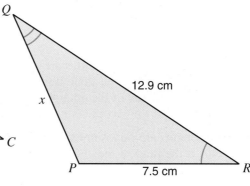

                                                                    OCR

4 Julie has made a scale model of St Bede's Church.
   The height of the model is 32 cm.
   The height of the real church is 16 m.
   (a) Work out the scale that Julie used.
        Write your answer in the form 1 : n.
   (b) The area of the floor of the church is 140 m².
        Work out the area of the floor of the model.
        Write your answer in square centimetres.

                                                                    OCR

5

   These tops are similar.
   The height of the small top is 6 cm.
   The height of the large top is 9 cm.

   (a) Find the ratio of the surface area of the small top to
        the surface area of the large top.
   (b) The volume of the large top is 135 cm³.
        Calculate the volume of the small top.

6 A metal sphere has a mass of 250 kg.
   It is melted down and used to make smaller spheres with a radius one fifth of the original.
   No metal is wasted.
   (a) Calculate the mass of each of the smaller spheres.

   The surface area of the large sphere is 4500 cm².
   (b) Calculate the **total** surface area of the smaller spheres.   OCR

What you need to know

- Quantities which have both **size** and **direction** are called **vectors**.
  For example: **Displacement** – A combination of distance and direction.

- **Vector notation**
  Vectors can be represented by **column vectors** or by **directed line segments**.
  Vectors can be labelled using:
    capital letters to indicate the start and finish of a vector,
    bold lower case letters.

  In a **column vector**:
    The top number describes the **horizontal** part of the movement.
    The bottom number describes the **vertical** part of the movement. $\overrightarrow{AB} = \mathbf{a} = \begin{pmatrix} 3 \\ 2 \end{pmatrix}$

- Vectors are **equal** if they have the same length **and** they are in the same direction.
  Vectors $\mathbf{a}$ and $-\mathbf{a}$ have the same length **but** are in **opposite directions**.
  The vector $n\mathbf{a}$ is parallel to the vector $\mathbf{a}$.
  The length of vector $n\mathbf{a} = n \times$ the length of vector $\mathbf{a}$.

- **Vector addition**
  The combination of the displacement from A to B followed by the displacement from B to C is
  equivalent to a total displacement from A to C.

  This can be written using vectors as $\overrightarrow{AB} + \overrightarrow{BC} = \overrightarrow{AC}$. $\overrightarrow{AC}$ is called the **resultant vector**.

- Combinations of vectors can be shown on **vector diagrams**.

  Eg 1 $\mathbf{a}$ and $\mathbf{b}$ are shown. Draw vectors to represent $\mathbf{a} + \mathbf{b}$ and $\mathbf{a} - \mathbf{b}$.

  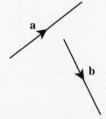 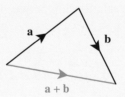 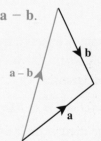

- You should be able to use **vector geometry** to solve simple geometrical problems,
  which can often involve parallel lines.

  Eg 2 $OAXB$ is a quadrilateral.

  $\overrightarrow{OA} = \mathbf{a}$, $\overrightarrow{OB} = \mathbf{b}$ and $\overrightarrow{AX} = 2\overrightarrow{OB}$.

  (a) Find, in terms of $\mathbf{a}$ and $\mathbf{b}$,

    (i) $\overrightarrow{AX}$,   (ii) $\overrightarrow{BX}$.

  (b) M and N are the midpoints of OA and BX respectively.

    (i) Find $\overrightarrow{MN}$, in terms of $\mathbf{a}$ and $\mathbf{b}$.
    (ii) What can you say about the lines OB and MN?
    (iii) What type of quadrilateral is $OMNB$?

  (a) (i) $\overrightarrow{AX} = 2\mathbf{b}$ (ii) $\overrightarrow{BX} = \mathbf{a} + \mathbf{b}$

  (b) (i) $\overrightarrow{MN} = 1\frac{1}{2}\mathbf{b}$ (ii) $2\overrightarrow{MN} = 3\overrightarrow{OB}$ (iii) Trapezium
                    MN is parallel to OB.

    The diagrams in this exercise have not been drawn accurately.

1 In the diagram, $\overrightarrow{OX} = \mathbf{x}$ and $\overrightarrow{OY} = \mathbf{y}$.

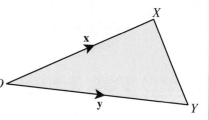

  (a) Write, in terms of $\mathbf{x}$ and $\mathbf{y}$, the vector $\overrightarrow{XY}$.

  (b) P and Q are the midpoints of OX and OY respectively.

      Find, in terms of $\mathbf{x}$ and $\mathbf{y}$, the vector $\overrightarrow{QP}$.

2 A is the point $(-3, 5)$ and B is the point $(3, 1)$.

  (a) Find $\overrightarrow{AB}$ as a column vector.

   C and D are points such that $\overrightarrow{CB} = \begin{pmatrix} -2 \\ -3 \end{pmatrix}$, and $ABCD$ is a trapezium with $\overrightarrow{AB} = 2\overrightarrow{DC}$.

  (b) Find the coordinates of D.

3 $ABCD$ is a trapezium.

$\overrightarrow{AD} = 3\overrightarrow{BC}$, $\overrightarrow{AB} = \mathbf{p}$ and $\overrightarrow{BC} = \mathbf{q}$.

Express, in terms of $\mathbf{p}$ and $\mathbf{q}$,   (a) $\overrightarrow{AD}$

                               (b) $\overrightarrow{CD}$

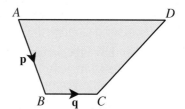

OCR

4 In the diagram,

$\overrightarrow{OC} = 2\overrightarrow{CA}$, $\overrightarrow{OD} = 2\overrightarrow{DB}$, $\overrightarrow{OA} = 3\mathbf{a}$, $\overrightarrow{OB} = 3\mathbf{b}$.

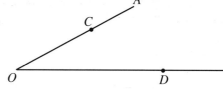

  (a) Work out, in terms of $\mathbf{a}$ and $\mathbf{b}$.

     (i) $\overrightarrow{OC}$ (ii) $\overrightarrow{AB}$ (iii) $\overrightarrow{CD}$

  (b) State two facts about the relationship between AB and CD.   OCR

5 In the diagram,

$\overrightarrow{OA} = \overrightarrow{AD} = \overrightarrow{CB} = \overrightarrow{BE} = \mathbf{a}$ and $\overrightarrow{OC} = \overrightarrow{AB} = \overrightarrow{DE} = \mathbf{c}$.

F is one third of the way along AC.

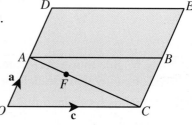

  (a) Find these vectors in terms of $\mathbf{a}$ and $\mathbf{c}$.
     Simplify your answers where possible.

     (i) $\overrightarrow{OE}$ (ii) $\overrightarrow{AC}$ (iii) $\overrightarrow{OF}$

  (b) What two facts can you conclude about the points O, F and E?   OCR

6 In the diagram, OAB is a triangle with $\overrightarrow{OA} = \mathbf{a}$ and $\overrightarrow{OB} = \mathbf{b}$.

P is the midpoint of OA and Q is the midpoint of AB.

M divides OQ in the ratio $2 : 1$.

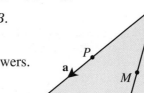

  (a) Find, in terms of $\mathbf{a}$ and $\mathbf{b}$, simplifying your answers.

     (i) $\overrightarrow{OQ}$,   (ii) $\overrightarrow{OM}$,

    (iii) $\overrightarrow{PB}$,   (iv) $\overrightarrow{PM}$.

  (b) What do you conclude about the point M and the line PB?   OCR

Further Trigonometry

What you need to know

- The graphs of the trigonometric functions.

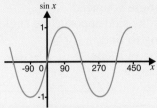 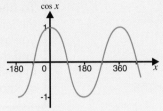 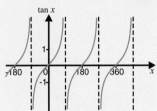

The **sine function** is a periodic function with period 360°.
$-1 \leqslant \sin x \leqslant 1$

The **cosine function** is a periodic function with period 360°.
$-1 \leqslant \cos x \leqslant 1$

The **tangent function** is a periodic function with period 180°.
Tan x is undefined at 90°, 270°, ...

- For every angle $x°$, the signs of $\sin x°$, $\cos x°$ and $\tan x°$ can be shown on a diagram.

  Positive angles are measured **anticlockwise**.
  Negative angles are measured **clockwise**.

  For angles greater than 360°: subtract 360°, or multiples of 360°, to get the equivalent angle between 0° and 360°.

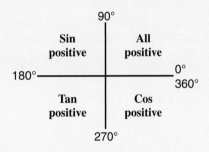

Eg 1 Sin 53.1° = 0.8, correct to 1 d.p.
  (a) Write down the other value of x for which $\sin x = 0.8$ for $0° \leqslant x \leqslant 360°$.
  (b) Solve the equation $\sin x = -0.8$ for $0° \leqslant x \leqslant 360°$.

(a) | Always work from 0° or 180° or 360°. When sin x is positive: $\sin x = \sin (180° - x)$ |

$x = 180° - 53.1° = 126.9°$

(b) | Sin x is negative, so values of x lie between 180° and 360° |

$x = 180° + 53.1° = 233.1°$
$x = 360° - 53.1° = 306.9°$
So, $x = 233.1°$ or $306.9°$

- The **exact values** of the trigonometric ratios for the angles 30°, 45° and 60° can be found from the triangles below.

 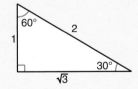

	30°	45°	60°
sin	$\dfrac{1}{2}$	$\dfrac{1}{\sqrt{2}}$	$\dfrac{\sqrt{3}}{2}$
cos	$\dfrac{\sqrt{3}}{2}$	$\dfrac{1}{\sqrt{2}}$	$\dfrac{1}{2}$
tan	$\dfrac{1}{\sqrt{3}}$	1	$\sqrt{3}$

- You should be able to use the **sine rule** and the **cosine rule** to solve problems involving triangles which are not right-angled.

- **The Sine Rule**

$$\frac{a}{\sin A} = \frac{b}{\sin B} = \frac{c}{\sin C}$$

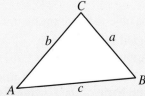

This can also be written as: $\dfrac{\sin A}{a} = \dfrac{\sin B}{b} = \dfrac{\sin C}{c}$

Eg 2 Calculate the length of side a.

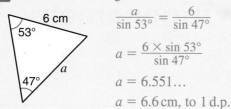

$$\frac{a}{\sin 53°} = \frac{6}{\sin 47°}$$

$$a = \frac{6 \times \sin 53°}{\sin 47°}$$

$$a = 6.551...$$

$$a = 6.6 \, \text{cm, to 1 d.p.}$$

To find a **side** you need:
two angles of known size, **and** the length of a side which is opposite one of the known angles.

Eg 3 Calculate the size of angle P.

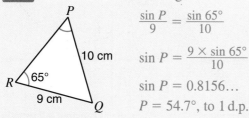

$$\frac{\sin P}{9} = \frac{\sin 65°}{10}$$

$$\sin P = \frac{9 \times \sin 65°}{10}$$

$$\sin P = 0.8156...$$

$$P = 54.7°, \text{ to 1 d.p.}$$

To find an **angle** you need:
the length of the side opposite the angle you are trying to find, **and** the length of a side opposite an angle of known size.

● **The Cosine Rule**

$$a^2 = b^2 + c^2 - 2bc \cos A$$

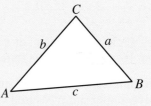

When using the Cosine Rule to find the size of an angle it is sometimes easier to rearrange the above formula as:

$$\cos A = \frac{b^2 + c^2 - a^2}{2bc}$$

Eg 4 Calculate the length of side x.

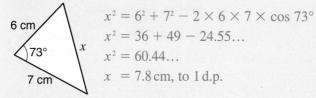

$$x^2 = 6^2 + 7^2 - 2 \times 6 \times 7 \times \cos 73°$$

$$x^2 = 36 + 49 - 24.55...$$

$$x^2 = 60.44...$$

$$x = 7.8 \, \text{cm, to 1 d.p.}$$

To find a **side** you need:
two sides of known length, **and** the size of the angle between the known sides.

Eg 5 Calculate the size of angle A.

$$\cos A = \frac{6^2 + 8^2 - 7^2}{2 \times 6 \times 8}$$

$$\cos A = 0.53125$$

$$A = 57.9°, \text{ to 1 d.p.}$$

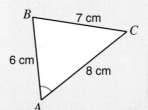

To find an **angle** you need:
three sides of known length.

● You should be able to find the area of a triangle which is not right-angled.

Eg 6 Calculate the area of triangle PQR.

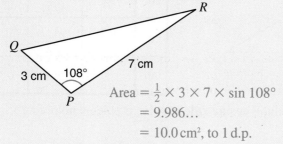

$$\text{Area} = \frac{1}{2} \times 3 \times 7 \times \sin 108°$$

$$= 9.986...$$

$$= 10.0 \, \text{cm}^2, \text{ to 1 d.p.}$$

To find the **area of a triangle** you need:
two sides of known length, **and** the size of the angle between the known sides.

$$\text{Area} = \frac{1}{2} ab \sin C.$$

● You should be able to solve problems involving triangles.

For **right-angled triangles** use:
the **trigonometric ratios** (sin, cos and tan), **Pythagoras' Theorem**.

For **triangles which are not right-angled** use:
the **Sine Rule** or the **Cosine Rule**.

Do not use a calculator for question 1.

1 (a) Cos 60° = 0.5

  (i) Write down the other value of x for which cos x = 0.5 for 0° ≤ x ≤ 360°.

  (ii) Solve the equation cos x = −0.5 for 0° ≤ x ≤ 360°.

 (b) (i) On the same diagram, sketch the graphs of y = cos x and y = sin x
   for 0° ≤ x ≤ 360°.

  (ii) Hence, solve the equation cos x = sin x for 0° ≤ x ≤ 360°.

2 Ship A is 10 km due North of lighthouse L.
Ship B is 12 km from A and is on a bearing of 056° from L.

Calculate the bearing of B from A.

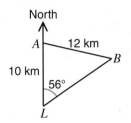

OCR

3
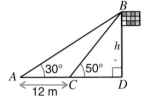

The diagram shows a vertical flagpole of height h metres standing on horizontal ground.

Calculate the height, h, of the flagpole.

OCR

4 In triangle ABC, D is the point on CB such that $AC = AD$.
AB = 11.1 cm, AC = 5.1 cm and DB = 7.9 cm.

Calculate the length of CD.

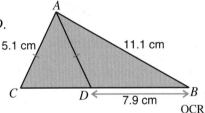

OCR

5
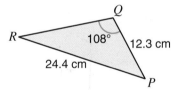

In the triangle PQR, angle PQR = 108°.
PQ = 12.3 cm and PR = 24.4 cm.

 (a) Calculate angle QRP.
 (b) Calculate the area of triangle PQR.

6 Ship A is 37.8 km from port P on a bearing of 051°.
Ship B is 54.9 km from port P on a bearing of 117°.

 (a) Calculate the distance AB.
 (b) Calculate the bearing of A from B.

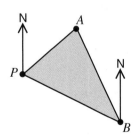

OCR

7
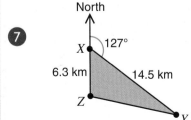

The diagram shows the positions of ships X, Y and Z.
X is 6.3 km due North of Z.
Y is 14.5 km from X on a bearing of 127°.

Calculate the distance and bearing of Z from Y.

8 In the triangle ABC, AB = 6 cm and AC = 9 cm.
The area of triangle ABC is 24 cm².

 (a) Calculate the two possible values of angle BAC.
 (b) Calculate the length of BC, when angle BAC is obtuse.

Shape, Space and Measures
Non-calculator Paper

Do not use a calculator for this exercise.

1 Work out the area of each shape.

(a)

3 cm

12 cm

(b)

8 cm

2 cm

5 cm

3 cm

2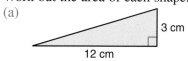

A ——————— B

140°

40°

C ——————— D

Give a reason why *AB* is parallel to *CD*.

OCR

3 (a) During a tropical rainstorm, 2 cm of rain fell into a rectangular tank.
The base of the tank measures 40 cm by 30 cm.
(i) Calculate the volume of water in the tank.
(ii) Change your answer to part (a)(i) into litres.

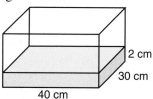

2 cm

30 cm

40 cm

(b) On another day, 2000 cm³ of water was collected
in a different tank.
The base of this tank is a square of side 20 cm.
Calculate the depth of the water in the tank.

OCR

4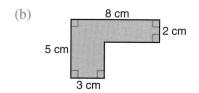

C

10 km   13 km

A   16 km   B

N

The diagram shows the positions of three towns, *A*, *B* and *C*.
B is 16 km East of *A*.   *AC* = 10 km   and   *BC* = 13 km.

(a) Make an accurate scale drawing of triangle *ABC*.
Use a scale of **1 cm to 2 km**.
(b) Use your drawing to find the bearing of *C* from *B*.

OCR

5 Copy the diagram onto squared paper.
(a) *P* is mapped onto *Q* by an enlargement, scale factor 2,
centre (−1, 3).
Draw and label *Q*.
(b) *P* is mapped onto *R* by a translation with vector $\begin{pmatrix} -3 \\ 2 \end{pmatrix}$.
Draw and label *R*.
(c) *P* is mapped onto *S* by a rotation through 90° clockwise,
about (1, 0).
Draw and label *S*.

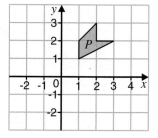

6 In the diagram, *ACF* is a straight line.
AD is parallel to *CE*.
AC = *BC*.

Calculate
(a) *x*,   (b) *y*,   (c) *z*.

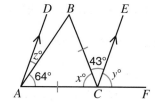

D   B   E

z°

64°

43°

x°   y°

A   C   F

OCR

7 (a) Construct triangle *ABC*, in which   *AB* = 9.5 cm,   *BC* = 8 cm   and   *CA* = 6 cm.
(b) Using ruler and compasses only, bisect angle *BAC*.
(c) Shade the region inside the triangle where all the points are less than 7.5 cm from *B*,
and nearer to *AC* than to *AB*.

8 These two cars are similar.
Calculate h, the height, of the smaller car.

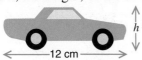
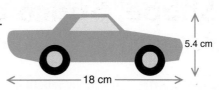

12 cm

h

18 cm

5.4 cm

9 A circle has an area of $49\,\pi\,\text{cm}^2$.
Calculate the circumference of the circle in terms of π.

10 The vertical height of a slide is 2.3 m, correct to the nearest 0.1 m.
Write down the minimum possible value of the vertical height.

OCR

11 The following formulae represent certain quantities connected with containers,
where a, b and c are dimensions.

$$\pi a \qquad abc \qquad \sqrt{a^2 - c^2} \qquad \pi a^2 b \qquad 2(a + b + c)$$

(a) Explain why abc represents a volume.
(b) Which of these formulae represent lengths?

12 (a) The roof of a barn is a prism.
The cross-section is an isosceles triangle.
The dimensions, in metres, are given on the diagram.
  (i) Show that $x = 5$.
  (ii) Work out the total surface area of the four sections
  of the barn roof.

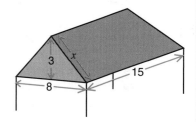

3

x

8

15

(b)

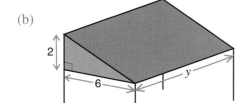

2

6

y

The roof of another barn is a triangular prism,
as shown in the diagram.
The dimensions, in metres, are given on the diagram.
The volume of the roof space is $48\,\text{m}^3$.
Work out the length of the roof, y metres.

OCR

13 (a) The two triangles on the right are congruent.
  (i) Find the length of x and the length of y.
  (ii) Explain how you found your answers.

(b) Are these two triangles similar?
Give reasons for your answer.

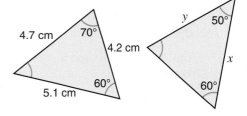

4.7 cm

70°

4.2 cm

60°

5.1 cm

y

50°

x

60°

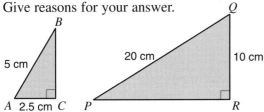

B

5 cm

A 2.5 cm C

Q

20 cm

P

10 cm

R

OCR

14 The diagram shows part of a regular polygon with
interior angles of 144°.
Work out the number of sides of the polygon.

144°

144°

OCR

15

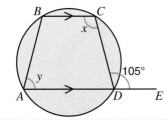

B

C

x

y

A D E

105°

ADE is a straight line.
BC is parallel to AE.

Work out angles x and y, giving reasons for your answers.

OCR

16 In the diagram ABC and AED are straight lines.
BE is parallel to CD.
$AB = 3.2$ cm, $BE = 3.6$ cm,
$ED = 1.4$ cm and $DC = 5.4$ cm.
Calculate
(a) the length of AC,   (b) the length of AE.

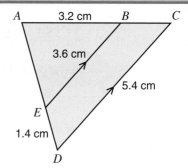

17

Tan $XYZ = \frac{4}{3}$.

(a) Find (i) sin XYZ,
        (ii) cos XYZ.
(b) When $XZ = 10$ cm, what are the lengths of XY and YZ?

18 (a) Given that $\mathbf{s} = \begin{pmatrix} 3 \\ 4 \end{pmatrix}$ and $\mathbf{t} = \begin{pmatrix} 6 \\ -1 \end{pmatrix}$, find $2\mathbf{s} - \mathbf{t}$.

(b) In the diagram $\overrightarrow{XQ} = 3\overrightarrow{PX}$.

Given that $\overrightarrow{PX} = \mathbf{p}$, find, in terms of $\mathbf{p}$,
(i) $\overrightarrow{XQ}$,   (ii) $\overrightarrow{QP}$.

(c) In the diagram, $ABCD$ is a parallelogram.
M and N are the midpoints of AB and DC.
$AB = \mathbf{a}$ and $AD = \mathbf{b}$.

Use a vector method to prove that $AMCN$
is also a parallelogram.

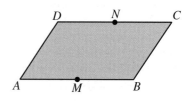

OCR

19

A hemispherical bowl has a diameter of 18 cm.

Calculate the volume of the bowl.
Give your answer in terms of π.

20 The diagram shows the image of an object after
an enlargement, scale factor $-\frac{1}{3}$, centre $(0, 0)$.

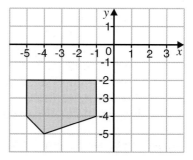

(a) Copy the diagram onto a grid with x and y axes
from -5 to 15.
Draw the object.
(b) How many times larger than the image is the
area of the object?

OCR

21 (a) Sketch a graph of $y = \cos x°$ for $-90 \leqslant x \leqslant 360$.
(b) Given that $\cos 30° = 0.866$, find the value of $\cos 210°$.
(c) Given that $\cos 60° = 0.5$, solve the equation $\cos x° = 0.5$ for $-90 \leqslant x \leqslant 360$.

OCR

22

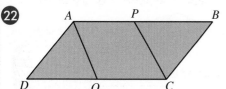

In the diagram, $ABCD$ is a parallelogram.
P and Q are the midpoints of AB and DC respectively.

(a) Prove that triangle PBC is congruent to triangle QDA.
(b) Prove that AQ is parallel to PC.

OCR

23 The diagram shows a piece of card.
The card is the major sector of a circle of radius 5 cm with a
concentric sector of radius 4 cm removed.
The angle of the sector is $320°$.
Find the area of the card, leaving your answer in terms of π.

OCR

You may use a calculator for this exercise.

1

(a) Copy the diagram.
Shade one more square so that the final diagram has line symmetry only.

(b) Make another copy of the diagram.
Shade one more square so that the final diagram has rotational symmetry only.

2 (a) Part of a tessellation of triangles is shown.
Copy the diagram.
Continue the tessellation by drawing four more triangles.

(b) Do all regular polygons tessellate?
Give a reason for your answer.

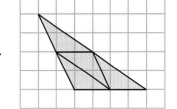

3 (a) A cuboid measures 2 cm by 2.5 cm by 4 cm.
(i) Draw an accurate net of the cuboid.
(ii) Calculate the total surface area of the cuboid.

(b) Another cuboid has a volume of 50 cm³.
The base of the cuboid measures 4 cm by 5 cm.
Calculate the height of the cuboid.

4 (a) In the diagram, $AB = AC$, angle $A = 98°$
and BCD is a straight line.
(i) Find the value of x.
(ii) Find the value of y.
Give a reason for your answer.

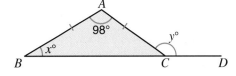

(b) $ABCD$ is a trapezium.
(i) Find the value of z.
Give a reason for your answer.
(ii) $AB = 24$ cm. $DC = 35$ cm.
The perpendicular distance between
AB and DC is 5 cm.
Find the area of the trapezium $ABCD$.

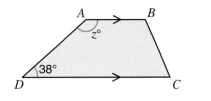

OCR

5 A circular plate has a diameter of 8 cm. Calculate the area of the plate.

6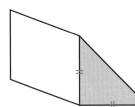

The diagram represents a prism.
The cross-section of the prism is an isosceles triangle.
Copy the diagram and draw one plane of symmetry of the prism.

7 The diagram shows the angle formed when three regular polygons
are placed together, as shown.
(a) Explain why angle a is 120°.
(b) Work out the size of the angle marked b.

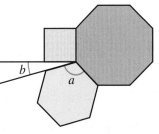

8 On a map the distance between two towns is 8.6 cm.
The map has been drawn to a scale of 1 to 250 000.
Calculate the actual distance between the towns in kilometres.

9

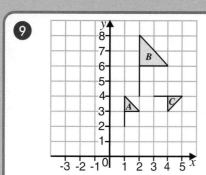

(a) Copy flag *A* onto squared paper.
Draw the image of the flag *A* after a translation $\begin{pmatrix} -4 \\ 3 \end{pmatrix}$.
Label it *T*.

(b) Describe fully the single transformation that will map
  (i) *A* onto *B*,   (ii) *A* onto *C*.

OCR

10 The diagram shows a plot of land.
The measurements are in metres.

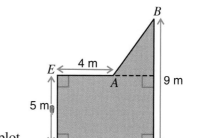

(a) The plot is to be turfed to make a lawn.
What will be the area of the lawn?

(b) (i) Find the length *AB*.
  (ii) A fence is to be put around the perimeter of the plot.
    What will be the length of the fence?

OCR

11

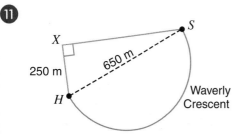

The diagram shows Fay's house, *H*, and her school, *S*.
To get to school Fay has a choice of two routes.
She can either walk along Waverly Crescent
or along the footpaths *HX* and *XS*.
Waverly Crescent is a semi-circle with diameter 650 m.
The footpath *HX* is 250 m and meets the footpath *XS*
at right-angles.
Which of these routes is shorter? By how much?

12 The diagram shows a block of wood which is 2 metres long.
The block is a prism with cross-section in the
shape of a trapezium.
Find the volume of the block.

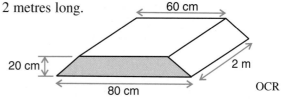

OCR

13

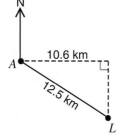

A ship at *A* is 12.5 km from a lighthouse (*L*).
A is 10.6 km West of *L*.

(a) Calculate the bearing of *L* from *A*.

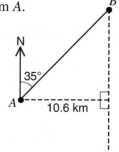

(b) The ship sails from *A* to *B*, where *B* is due North of *L*.
The bearing of *B* from *A* is 035°.

Calculate the distance *AB*.

OCR

14

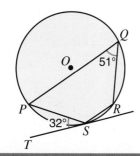

O is the centre of the circle.
P, *Q*, *R* and *S* are points on the circumference of the circle.
Angle *PQR* = 51°.
(a) Work out angle *PSR*, giving a reason for your answer.

TS is a tangent to the circle at *S*.
Angle *PST* = 32°.
(b) Find angle *PRS*, giving a reason for your answer.

OCR

15 Copy the diagram.

    (a) Enlarge shape S, centre $(-1, 2)$, scale factor -2. Label the image T.

    (b) Describe the single transformation which maps T onto S.

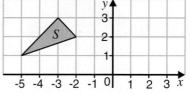

16

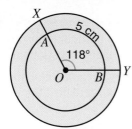

The diagram shows two concentric circles with centre O.
$\angle XOY = 118°$. $OX = 8.5\,\text{cm}$.

    (a) Calculate the area of the sector XOY.

    (b) The arc $AB = 5\,\text{cm}$. Calculate OA.

17 In the diagram $\overrightarrow{OA} = \mathbf{a}$ and $\overrightarrow{OB} = \mathbf{b}$.
B is the midpoint of OX.

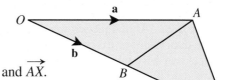

    (a) Find, in terms of $\mathbf{a}$ and $\mathbf{b}$, the vectors $\overrightarrow{OX}$ and $\overrightarrow{AX}$.

    (b) M is the midpoint of AX. Prove that BM is parallel to OA.

18 $ABCD$ is the top and $EFGH$ is the bottom of a rectangular box.
The width $EH = 15\,\text{cm}$, the length $HG = 30\,\text{cm}$ and the height $AE = 13\,\text{cm}$.

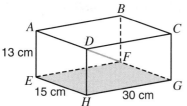

    (a) Calculate the length of the diagonal DF.

    (b) Calculate the angle between the diagonal, DF, and the base, $EFGH$.

OCR

19 $ABCD$ is a cyclic quadrilateral.
$AD = 5.3\,\text{cm}$, $DC = 2.9\,\text{cm}$, angle $ADC = 131°$ and $AB = BC$.

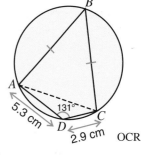

    (a) Calculate the length of AC.

    (b) What is the size of angle ABC?

    (c) Calculate the length of AB.

OCR

20

The stand on which the dog is sitting is the frustum of a cone.
The top of the stand has a radius of $0.5\,\text{m}$.
The bottom of the stand has a radius of $1\,\text{m}$.
The height of the stand is $0.6\,\text{m}$.

    (a) Calculate the volume of the stand.

    (b) The height of a similar stand is $0.4\,\text{m}$. Calculate the volume of this stand.

21 The diagram shows a triangular piece of card.
Angle BAC is obtuse, $AB = 5.8\,\text{cm}$ and $AC = 7.4\,\text{cm}$.
The area of the card is $20\,\text{cm}^2$.
Calculate the length of BC.
Give your answer to a suitable degree of accuracy.

22 The volume of a cylinder is given as $680\,\text{cm}^3$, correct to two significant figures.
The height is $9.6\,\text{cm}$ to the nearest millimetre.
Calculate the upper and lower bounds of the radius.

Collection and Organisation of Data

What you need to know

- **Primary data** is data collected by an individual or organisation to use for a particular purpose. Primary data is obtained from experiments, investigations, surveys and by using questionnaires.

- **Secondary data** is data which is already available or has been collected by someone else for a different purpose. Sources of secondary data include the Annual Abstract of Statistics, Social Trends and the Internet.

- **Qualitative** data – Data which can only be described in words.   E.g. Colour of cars.

- **Quantitative** data – Data that has a numerical value.
  Quantitative data is either **discrete** or **continuous**.
  Discrete data can only take certain values.   E.g. Numbers of cars in car parks.
  Continuous data has no exact value and is measurable.   E.g. Weights of cars.

- **Data Collection Sheets** – Used to record data during a survey.

- **Tally** – A way of recording each item of data on a data collection sheet.

- **Frequency Table** – A way of collating the information recorded on a data collection sheet.

- **Grouped Frequency Table** – Used for continuous data or for discrete data when a lot of data has to be recorded.

- **Database** – A collection of data.

- **Class Interval** – The width of the groups used in a grouped frequency distribution.

- **Questionnaire** – A set of questions used to collect data for a survey.
  Questionnaires should: (1) use simple language,
                    (2) ask short questions which can be answered precisely,
                    (3) provide tick boxes,
                    (4) avoid open-ended questions,
                    (5) avoid leading questions,
                    (6) ask questions in a logical order.

- **Hypothesis** – A hypothesis is a statement which may or may not be true.

- When information is required about a large group of people it is not always possible to survey everyone and only a **sample** may be asked.
  The sample chosen should be large enough to make the results meaningful and representative of the whole group (population) or the results may be **biased**.

- **Two-way Tables** – A way of illustrating two features of a survey.

- In a **simple random sample** everyone has an equal chance of being selected.

- In a **systematic random sample** people are selected according to some rule.

- In a **stratified random sample** the original group is divided up into separate categories or strata, such as male/female, age group, etc, before a random sample is taken. A simple random sample is then taken from each category in proportion to the size of the category.

Exercise 35

1. To find out how long students spend on homework each night, Pat asks a class of Year 7 students how much time they spent on their homework last night.
   Give two reasons why his results may not be typical of all students.

2 Julie is writing questions for a survey. Her hypothesis is that the main reason why people live in the Sharrow area is the cost of housing.
This is one of her questions.

Do you agree that the cost of housing is the main reason that people live in the Sharrow area, and if not, what do you think is the main reason?

State two things wrong with this question.

OCROCR

3 This sample was used to investigate the claim: **"Women do more exercise than men."**

	Age (years)			
	16 to 21	22 to 45	46 to 65	Over 65
Male	5	5	13	7
Female	25	35	0	0

Give three reasons why the sample is biased.

4 The table shows the results of a survey of 500 people.

	Can drive	Cannot drive
Men	180	20
Women	240	60

200
300

A newspaper headline states: **Survey shows that more women can drive than men.**
Do the results of the survey support this headline? Men = 180 ÷ 200 = 90%.
Give a reason for your answer. women 240 ÷ 300 = 80%

5 The two-way table shows the results of a survey of the number of cats and the number of dogs people have as pets.

Number of cats

		0	1	2	3
Number of dogs	0	21	9	3	0
	1	5	4	(2)	0
	2	2	1	0	1
	3	1	1	0	0

(a) How many people have one dog **and** two cats as pets? 2
(b) A magazine article stated, *"Cats are more popular than dogs as pets."*
    Does this survey support that claim? Give a reason for your answer.
(c) How many dogs did these people have altogether?

6 The pupils of form 7A are to conduct a survey about students' preferences in music in their school.
(a) Jenny decides to ask every tenth person who walks through one of the school gates.
    Give two reasons why Jenny's method would not give a representative sample of the pupils in the school.
(b) Ahmed wants to select a stratified sample of the pupils.
    Explain how Ahmed could do this.

OCROCR

7 Peter conducts a survey of the students in his school.
He decides to interview 100 of the students.
The number of students in each year group of the school is given in the table below.

Year group	7	8	9	10	11
Number of students	142	154	115	127	102

Calculate the number of students he should choose from each year group to provide a representative sample.

OCROCR

Collection and Organisation of DataCollection and Organisation of Data

35

93

SECTION **36** **Averages and Range**

What you need to know

- There are three types of **average**: the **mode**, the **median** and the **mean**.
  The **mode** is the most common value.
  The **median** is the middle value (or the mean of the two middle values) when the values are arranged in order of size.

  The **Mean** $= \dfrac{\text{Total of all values}}{\text{Number of values}}$

- The **range** is a measure of **spread**, and is the difference between the highest and lowest values.

  Eg 1 The number of text messages received by 7 students on Saturday is shown.

  $$2 \quad 4 \quad 3 \quad 4 \quad 4 \quad 3 \quad 2$$

  Find (a) the mode, (b) the median, (c) the mean, (d) the range.

  (a) The mode is 4.

  (b) $2 \quad 2 \quad 3 \quad ③ \quad 4 \quad 4 \quad 4$ The median is 3.

  (c) The mean $= \dfrac{2 + 4 + 3 + 4 + 4 + 3 + 2}{7} = \dfrac{22}{7} = 3.14\ldots = 3.1$, correct to 1 d.p.

  (d) The range $= 4 - 2 = 2$

- To find the mean of a **frequency distribution** use: Mean $= \dfrac{\text{Total of all values}}{\text{Number of values}} = \dfrac{\Sigma fx}{\Sigma f}$

  Eg 2 The table shows the number of stamps on some parcels.

Number of stamps	1	2	3	4
Number of parcels	5	6	9	4

  Find the mean number of stamps per parcel.

  Mean $= \dfrac{\text{Total number of stamps}}{\text{Number of parcels}} = \dfrac{1 \times 5 + 2 \times 6 + 3 \times 9 + 4 \times 4}{5 + 6 + 9 + 4} = \dfrac{60}{24} = 2.5$

- To find the mean of a **grouped frequency distribution**, first find the value of the midpoint of each class.
  Then use:
  $$\text{Estimated mean} = \dfrac{\text{Total of all values}}{\text{Number of values}} = \dfrac{\Sigma fx}{\Sigma f}$$

  Eg 3 The table shows the weights of some parcels.

Weight (w grams)	Frequency
$100 \leqslant w < 200$	7
$200 \leqslant w < 300$	11
$300 \leqslant w < 400$	19
$400 \leqslant w < 500$	3

  Calculate an estimate of the mean weight of these parcels.

  Mean $= \dfrac{\Sigma fx}{\Sigma f} = \dfrac{150 \times 7 + 250 \times 11 + 350 \times 19 + 450 \times 3}{7 + 11 + 19 + 3} = \dfrac{11\,800}{40} = 295$ grams

- You should be able to choose the best average to use in different situations for different sets of data.

Do not use a calculator for question 1.

1 The prices paid for eight different meals at a restaurant are:

£10   £9   £9.50   £12   £20   £11.50   £11   £9

(a) Which price is the mode?
(b) Find the median price.
(c) Calculate the mean price.
(d) Which of these averages best describes the average price paid for a meal?
    Give a reason for your answer.

2 Mr Morgan looks at the maths examination results for two classes in year 11.

For class A: the mean mark is **58.5%**, the median is **58%**
              the modal mark is **63%**, the range is **29%**

These are the percentages for class B: **43, 44, 45, 45, 50, 53, 54, 59, 59, 60**
                                        62, 62, 62, 63, 64, 64, 64, 64, 70, 71

Mr Morgan thinks class B has the better results.
Use the data to give one reason why he may be right and one reason why he may be wrong.
Show all your working.   OCR

3 The mean weight of the 8 Forwards in a rugby team is 108.25 kg.
The mean weight of the 7 Backs in the team is 89.5 kg.
Calculate the mean weight of the 15 members of the team.   OCR

4 Helen and Reg play ten-pin bowling. The graph shows their scores for the first 10 frames.

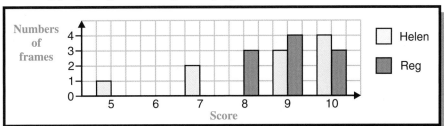

(a) What is the range in the scores for Helen?
(b) Find the mean of the scores for Reg.
(c) Reg says, "My average score is higher than Helen's."
    Helen says, "My average score is higher than Reg's."
    A friend says, "Your average scores are both the same."
    Which average is being used by each person? Show your working.

5 Darren throws a dice 60 times. His results are shown.

Score	1	2	3	4	5	6
Frequency	12	10	9	11	10	8

(a) For these results, find
    (i) the mode,   (ii) the median,   (iii) the mean.
(b) Darren throws the dice again and scores a 6.
    Which of the averages he has found will not change?

6 Jenny asked 200 people how much they spent last year on magazines.
The results are in the table below.

Amount (£x)	$0 < x \leqslant 10$	$10 < x \leqslant 20$	$20 < x \leqslant 30$	$30 < x \leqslant 40$	$40 < x \leqslant 50$
Frequency	40	50	48	30	32

(a) Calculate an estimate of the mean amount spent on magazines.
(b) Explain briefly why this value of the mean is only an estimate.   OCR

Presentation of Data 1 ●●●●

What you need to know

- **Bar chart**. Used for data which can be counted.
  Often used to compare quantities of data in a distribution.
  The length of each bar represents frequency.

  > Bars can be drawn horizontally or vertically.

- **Bar-line graph**. Instead of drawing bars, horizontal or vertical lines are drawn to show frequency.

- **Pie chart**. Used for data which can be counted.
  Often used to compare proportions of data, usually with the total.
  The whole circle represents all the data.
  The size of each sector represents the frequency of data in that sector.

  Eg 1 The results of asking a group of children which board game they liked best is shown.

Board game	Chess	Draughts	Ludo	Snakes & Ladders
Number of children	4	9	2	5

  Draw a pie chart to show this information.
  20 children were asked.
  Each child is represented by $\frac{360°}{20} = 18°$.

  Chess: $4 \times 18° = 72°$
  Draughts: $9 \times 18° = 162°$
  Ludo: $2 \times 18° = 36°$
  Snakes & Ladders: $5 \times 18° = 90°$

  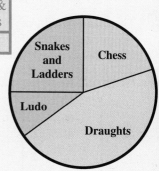

- **Stem and leaf diagrams**. Used to represent data in its original form.
  Data is split into two parts.
  The part with the higher place value is the stem.   E.g.   15 = stem 1, leaf 5.
  A key is given to show the value of the data.   E.g.   3|4 means 3.4, etc.
  The data is shown in numerical order on the diagram.   E.g.   2|3 5 9 represents 23, 25, 29.
  Back to back stem and leaf diagrams can be used to compare two sets of data.

  Eg 2 The times, in seconds, taken by 10 students to complete a puzzle are shown.
  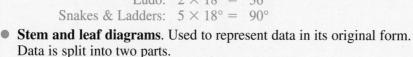
  9   23   17   20   12   11   24   12   10   26
  Construct a stem and leaf diagram to represent this information.

  ```
              2 | 0  means 20 seconds
      0 | 9
      1 | 0  1  2  2  7
      2 | 0  3  4  6
  ```

- A **scatter graph** can be used to show the relationship between two sets of data.
- The relationship between two sets of data is referred to as **correlation**.
- You should be able to recognise **positive** and **negative** correlation.
  The correlation is stronger as points get closer to a straight line.
- When there is a relationship between two sets of data a **line of best fit** can be drawn on the scatter graph.
- **Perfect correlation** is when all the points lie on a straight line.
- The line of best fit can be used to **estimate** the value from one set of the data when the corresponding value of the other set is known.

Positive correlation   Negative correlation

Eg 3 The table shows the weights and heights of 10 girls.

Weight (kg)	33	36	37	39	40	42	45	45	48	48
Height (cm)	133	134	137	140	146	146	145	150	152	156

(a) Draw a scatter graph for the data.
(b) What type of correlation is shown?
(c) Draw a line of best fit.
(d) A girl weighs 50 kg. Estimate her height.

> Mark a cross on the graph to show the weight and height of each girl.

(a)

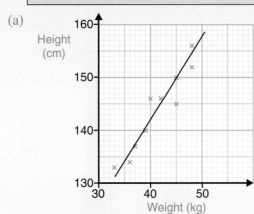

On a scatter graph:
The **slope** of the line of best fit shows the **trend** of the data.
The line of best fit does not have to go through the origin of the graph.

(b) Positive correlation.
(c) The line of best fit has been drawn, by eye, on the graph.
(d) 158 cm. Read estimate where 50 kg meets line of best fit.

Exercise 37

1 The stem and leaf diagram shows the highest November temperature recorded in 12 European countries last year.

```
                                    0 | 7   means 7°C
        0 | 7   9
        1 | 0   3   4   4   4   7   8
        2 | 0   1   2
```

(a) How many countries are included?
(b) What is the maximum temperature recorded?
(c) Which temperature is the mode?
(d) When the temperature in another European country is included in the data, the range increases by 2°C.
What was the temperature in that country? Explain your answer.

2 The scatter graphs show the results of a survey given to people on holiday at a seaside resort.

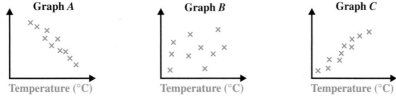

(a) Which scatter graph shows the temperature (°C) plotted against:
(i)   the number of people in the sea,
(ii) the number of people with coats on,
(iii) the amount of money people spend?
(b) Which scatter graph shows a positive correlation?

3 Pali asked 180 boys what was their favourite sport. Here are his results.

Sport	Soccer	Rugby	Cricket	Basketball	Other
Number of boys	74	25	18	37	26

(a) Draw a pie chart to show these results.

Pali also asked 90 girls about their favourite sport.
In a pie chart showing the results, the angle for Tennis was 84°.

(b) How many of these girls said that Tennis was their favourite sport?   OCR

4 The number of text messages Anila sent each day in the last two weeks is shown.

    7   12   10   5   21   11   9   2   17   3   5   13   20   15

(a) Construct a stem and leaf diagram to show this information.
(b) What is the range in the number of text messages Anila sent each day?

5 The bar chart shows information about the injuries of drivers involved in road accidents at a busy junction.

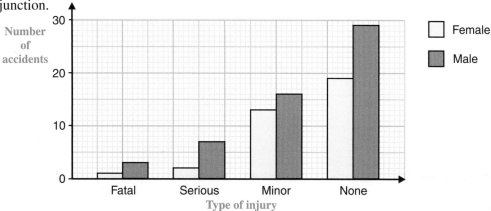

(a) What percentage of drivers had no injuries?
(b) Find, in its simple form, the ratio of female to male drivers involved in these accidents?
(c) Draw a pie chart to illustrate the proportion of drivers with each type of injury.

6 Twenty children were asked to estimate the length of a leaf.
Their estimates, in centimetres, are:

		Boys		
4.5	5.0	4.0	3.5	4.0
4.5	5.0	4.5	3.5	4.5

		Girls		
4.5	5.0	3.5	4.0	5.5
3.5	4.5	3.5	3.0	2.5

(a) Construct a back to back stem and leaf diagram to represent this information.
(b) Compare and comment on the estimates of these boys and girls.

7 A sports scientist asked eight members of a sports club how many hours per day, on average, each spent exercising.
He also also measured each member's resting pulse rate.
His results are shown in the table below.

Member	A	B	C	D	E	F	G	H
Hours spent on exercise	1.5	3.5	3	2.5	2	4	1	2
Resting pulse rate (beats/minute)	72	59	62	60	70	55	70	65

(a) Draw a scatter graph to show this information.
(b) Describe the correlation between the number of hours spent on exercise and the resting pulse rate of the members.
(c) Add a line of best fit to your scatter diagram.
(d) Another club member spends 6 hours per day exercising.
Explain why the line of best fit cannot be used to estimate his resting pulse rate.   OCR

Presentation of Data 2

What you need to know

- A **time series** is a set of readings taken at time intervals.

- A **line graph** is used to show a time series.

> Only the plotted points represent actual values. Points are joined by lines to show the **trend**.

- Variations in a time series which recur with the seasons of the year are called **seasonal variations**.

- **Moving averages** are used to smooth out variations in a time series so that the trend can be seen.

  Eg 1 The graph shows the amount of gas used by a householder each quarter over a period of 3 years.

  The blue crosses show the 4-quarterly moving average values.

  A line of best fit, drawn for the moving averages, shows the general **trend**.

  The trend shows a slight increase in the amount of gas used.

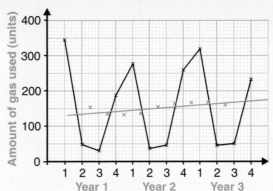

- **Frequency polygon**. Used to illustrate grouped frequency distributions. Often used to compare two or more distributions on the same diagram.

  Eg 2 The frequency distribution of the heights of some boys is shown.

Height (h cm)	$130 \leqslant h < 140$	$140 \leqslant h < 150$	$150 \leqslant h < 160$	$160 \leqslant h < 170$	$170 \leqslant h < 180$
Frequency	1	7	12	9	3

  Draw a frequency polygon to illustrate the data.

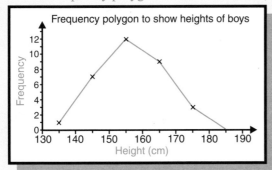

> Frequencies are plotted at the midpoints of the class intervals and joined with straight lines.

- **Histograms**. Used to illustrate grouped frequency distributions.
  The horizontal axis is a continuous scale.
  Bars are drawn between the lower and upper class boundaries for each class interval.
  When the classes have gaps between them the upper class boundary is halfway between the end of one class and the beginning of the next.

- Histograms can have equal or unequal class width intervals.
  With **equal** class width intervals: **frequency** is proportional to the **heights** of the bars.
  With **unequal** class width intervals: **frequency** is proportional to the **areas** of the bars.

> frequency = frequency density × class width interval

Eg 3 The times taken by 40 pupils to solve a puzzle are:

Time (t seconds)	$10 \leqslant t < 20$	$20 \leqslant t < 25$	$25 \leqslant t < 30$	$30 \leqslant t < 45$
Frequency	a) 6	b) 12	c) 10	d) 12

Draw a histogram to represent the data.

> **To find the height of each bar:**
> The height of each bar is given by the **frequency density** for each group, where:
>
> $$\text{frequency density} = \frac{\text{frequency}}{\text{class width interval}}$$
>
> E.g. For the group $10 \leqslant t < 20$: Frequency density $\frac{6}{10} = 0.6$
> Draw the bar to a height of 0.6

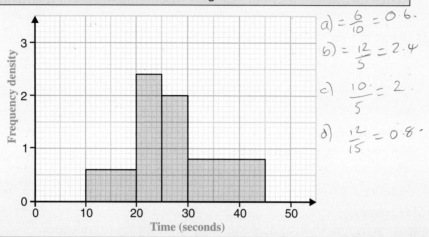

a) $= \frac{6}{10} = 0.6$

b) $= \frac{12}{5} = 2.4$

c) $\frac{10}{5} = 2$

d) $\frac{12}{15} = 0.8$

Exercise 38

1 The table shows the number of units of electricity used each quarter by a householder over a period of 3 years.

Year	2003				2004				2005			
Quarter	1	2	3	4	1	2	3	4	1	2	3	4
Units used	680	810	470	740	640	850	420	750	970	880	490	760

(a) Plot these values on graph paper.
(b) Calculate a 4-point moving average.
(c) Plot the moving average values on your graph.
(d) Comment on the trend in the units of electricity used.

2 The table shows the waiting times for patients in a doctor's surgery.

Waiting Time (t minutes)	Frequency
$0 \leqslant t < 4$	8
$4 \leqslant t < 8$	15
$8 \leqslant t < 12$	12
$12 \leqslant t < 16$	6
$16 \leqslant t < 20$	4
$20 \leqslant t < 24$	0

Draw a frequency diagram to show this information.

OCR

3 For this diagram, give two reasons why it may be misleading.

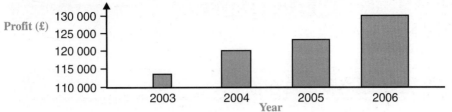

OCR

✗

4 The graph shows the age distribution of people in a nursing home.

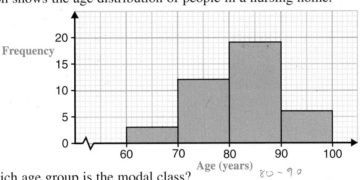

80-90

(a) Which age group is the modal class?

(b) How many people are in the nursing home? 3 + 12 + 19 + 6 = 40

(c) The table shows the age distribution of men in the home.

Age (a years)	$60 \leqslant a < 70$	$70 \leqslant a < 80$	$80 \leqslant a < 90$	$90 \leqslant a < 100$
Frequency	2	7	6	0

(i) Draw a frequency polygon to represent this information.

(ii) On the same diagram draw a frequency polygon to represent the age distribution of women in the home.

(iii) Compare and comment on the ages of men and women in the home.

✗

5 The histogram shows how long it took a sample of students to complete their mathematics homework on one evening. 28   9   5   5   3 = 50.

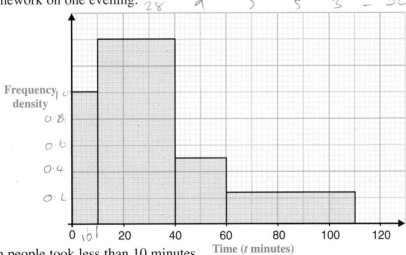

Ten people took less than 10 minutes.

Estimate how many people took more than 20 minutes.   50-ish

OCR

✗

6 The lengths of times that CD players worked before developing a fault is shown.

Time (t years)	$0 < t \leqslant 1$	$1 < t \leqslant 2$	$2 < t \leqslant 5$	$5 < t \leqslant 10$
Frequency	18	52	21	15

Draw a histogram to represent these data.

OCR

Cumulative Frequency

What you need to know

- The information given in a frequency table can be used to make a **cumulative frequency table**.
- You should be able to **draw cumulative frequency graphs**.

To draw a cumulative frequency graph:
1. Draw and label:
   the variable on the horizontal axis,
   cumulative frequency on the vertical axis.
2. Plot the cumulative frequency against the upper class boundary of each class.
3. Join the points with a smooth curve.

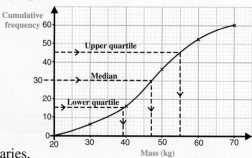

- If the question does not give the upper class boundaries, then the upper class boundary of each class is equal to the lower class boundary of the next class.
- When the classes have gaps between them then the upper class boundary is halfway between the end of one class and the beginning of the next.
- You should be able to **interpret cumulative frequency graphs**.

The **median** is the value of the middle number.

The **lower quartile** is the value located at $\frac{1}{4}$ of the total frequency.

The **upper quartile** is the value located at $\frac{3}{4}$ of the total frequency.

The **interquartile range** measures the spread of the middle 50% of the data.

Interquartile range = Upper Quartile − Lower Quartile

Eg 1 The times spent by students on the Internet one day are shown.

Time (t minutes)	$0 \leqslant t < 20$	$20 \leqslant t < 40$	$40 \leqslant t < 60$	$60 \leqslant t < 80$
Frequency	55	25	15	5

(a) Draw a cumulative frequency graph.
(b) Use your graph to find:
   (i) the median,
   (ii) the interquartile range.

(a)   Make a cumulative frequency table that can be used to draw the graph.

Time (mins) less than	0	20	40	60	80
Cumulative frequency	0	55	80	95	100

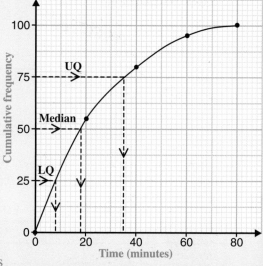

(b) Reading from the graph:
   (i) Median = 18 minutes
   (ii) Lower quartile (LQ) = 8 minutes
       Upper quartile (UQ) = 35 minutes
       Interquartile range = UQ − LQ = 35 − 8 = 27 minutes

- A **box plot** is used to represent the range, the median and the quartiles of a distribution.

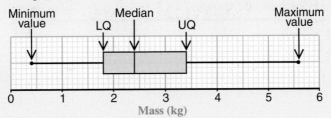

Mass (kg)

- The box plot shows how the data is spread out and how the middle 50% of data is clustered.

- Box plots can be used to compare two (or more) distributions.

- You should be able to draw and interpret box plots.

Eg 2 15 pupils were asked to estimate the size of an angle.
Their estimates, in degrees, are shown.

40   20   38   30   32   45   35   36   40   35   30   40   45   42   25

Draw a box plot to illustrate the data.

> Put the data in order and locate the median, lower quartile and upper quartile.
> Then use these values to draw the box plot.

20   25   30   ⃝30   32   35   35   ⃝36   38   40   40   ⃝40   42   45   45

LQ   Median   UQ

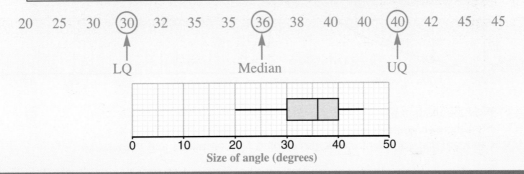

Size of angle (degrees)

Exercise 39

1   As part of a lifesaving course a group of students were asked to swim as far as possible
    wearing shoes and clothes.
    The cumulative frequency graph shows the distances swum.

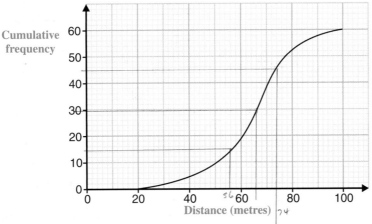

(a) Use the graph to find: 66m
     (i) the median distance,   (ii) the interquartile range. 74 − 56 = 18
(b) Draw a box plot to illustrate the distances swum.

Cumulative Frequency

2 A group of children were asked to estimate the weight of a bucket of water. Their estimates, in kilograms, are shown.

10	9	17.5	8	7.5	5	10	15
12.5	20	8	10	14	18	11	

(a) Find (i) the median estimate, (ii) the interquartile range of these estimates.
(b) Draw a box plot to represent these estimates.

3 The cumulative frequency graphs show information about the prices paid for computers and televisions.

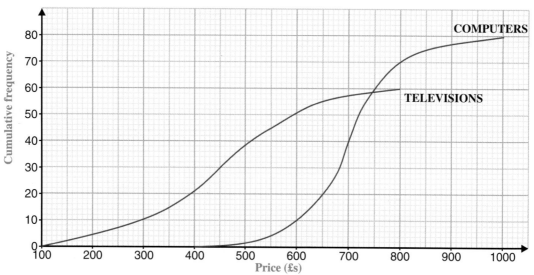

(a) Find the median price paid for a television.
(b) Find the interquartile range of the prices paid for computers.
(c) Compare and comment on the prices paid for computers and televisions.

4 The box plots illustrate the distribution of weights for a sample of eating apples and a sample of cooking apples.

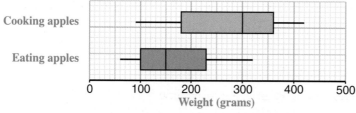

(a) What is the range in the weights of the eating apples?
(b) Which type of apple has the higher median weight?
(c) What is the interquartile range for cooking apples?
(d) Compare and comment on these distributions.

5 Tasmin asked 100 people with computers how long they spent on the Internet one Saturday. This table shows her results.

Number of hours (t)	$0 < t \leqslant 2$	$2 < t \leqslant 4$	$4 < t \leqslant 6$	$6 < t \leqslant 8$	$8 < t \leqslant 10$
Number or people	5	24	33	28	10

(a) Draw a cumulative frequency graph to show her results.
(b) Find the median length of time spent by these people on the Internet.
(c) How many of these people spent within one hour above or below the median time on the Internet?
Show how you found your answer.

OCR

Probability

What you need to know

- **Probability** describes how likely or unlikely it is that an event will occur. Probabilities are written as **fractions**, **decimals** or **percentages**.

- How to work out probabilities using **equally likely outcomes**.

$$\text{The probability of an event} = \frac{\text{Number of outcomes in the event}}{\text{Total number of possible outcomes}}$$

Eg 1 A box contains 7 red pens and 4 blue pens. A pen is taken from the box at random. What is the probability that the pen is blue?

$$P(\text{blue}) = \frac{\text{Number of blue pens}}{\text{Total number of pens}} = \frac{4}{11}$$

> P(blue) stands for the probability that the pen is blue.

- How to estimate probabilities using **relative frequency**.

$$\text{Relative frequency} = \frac{\text{Number of times the event happens in an experiment (or in a survey)}}{\text{Total number of trials in the experiment (or observations in the survey)}}$$

Eg 2 A spinner is spun 20 times. The results are shown.

| 4 | 1 | 3 | 1 | 4 | 2 | 2 | 4 | 3 | 3 |
| 4 | 1 | 4 | 4 | 3 | 2 | 2 | 1 | 3 | 2 |

What is the relative frequency of getting a 4?

$$\text{Relative frequency} = \frac{\text{Number of 4's}}{\text{Number of spins}} = \frac{6}{20} = 0.3$$

> Relative frequency gives a better estimate of probability the larger the number of trials.

- How to use probabilities to **estimate** the number of times an event occurs in an **experiment** or **observation**.

$$\text{Estimate} = \text{total number of trials (or observations)} \times \text{probability of event}$$

Eg 3 1000 raffle tickets are sold. Alan buys some tickets.
The probability that Alan wins first prize is $\frac{1}{50}$.
How many tickets did Alan buy? Number of tickets = $1000 \times \frac{1}{50} = 20$

- **Mutually exclusive events** cannot occur at the same time.

$$\text{When A and B are mutually exclusive events:}\quad P(A \text{ or } B) = P(A) + P(B)$$

Eg 4 A box contains red, green, blue and yellow counters.
The table shows the probability of getting each colour.

Colour	Red	Green	Blue	Yellow
Probability	0.4	0.25	0.25	0.1

A counter is taken from the box at random.
What is the probability of getting a red or blue counter?

$P(\text{Red or Blue}) = P(\text{Red}) + P(\text{Blue}) = 0.4 + 0.25 = 0.65$

- $$\text{The probability of an event, A, \textbf{not happening} is:}\quad P(\text{not } A) = 1 - P(A)$$

For example, the probability I will get a phone call today is 0.9.
So, the probability I will **not** get a phone call today is $1 - 0.9 = 0.1$.

- How to find all the possible outcomes when two events are combined.
  - By **listing** the outcomes systematically.
  - By using a **possibility space diagram**.
  - By using a **tree diagram**.

- The outcomes of **independent events** do not influence each other.

> When A and B are independent events: $P(A \text{ and } B) = P(A) \times P(B)$

Eg 5 Box A contains 3 white cubes (W) and 1 blue cube (B).
Box B contains 2 white cubes (W) and 3 blue cubes (B).
A cube is drawn from each box at random.
(a) Draw a tree diagram to show all the possible outcomes.
(b) Calculate the probability of getting two white cubes.

(a)
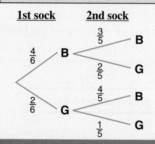

Box A	**Box B**	**Outcome**

(b)

> To calculate P(WW), multiply the probabilities along the branches of the tree diagram.

$$P(WW) = \tfrac{3}{4} \times \tfrac{2}{5}$$
$$= \tfrac{6}{20}$$
$$= \tfrac{3}{10}$$

- **Conditional probabilities** arise when the probabilities of particular events occurring are affected by other events.

Eg 6 In a drawer there are 4 black socks and 2 green socks. Two socks are taken at random. What is the probability that they are both the same colour?

> The probabilities for the second sock are **dependent** on the colour of the first sock.

1st sock	**2nd sock**

$\frac{4}{6}$ B $\frac{3}{5}$ B $\frac{2}{5}$ G

$\frac{2}{6}$ G $\frac{4}{5}$ B $\frac{1}{5}$ G

$$P(\text{same colour}) = P(BB) + P(GG)$$
$$= \left(\tfrac{4}{6} \times \tfrac{3}{5}\right) + \left(\tfrac{2}{6} \times \tfrac{1}{5}\right)$$
$$= \tfrac{12}{30} + \tfrac{2}{30}$$
$$= \tfrac{14}{30} = \tfrac{7}{15}$$
$$P(\text{same colour}) = \tfrac{7}{15}$$

Exercise 40

1 (a) Marco is recycling his glass bottles.
He has one green (G), one brown (B) and one clear (C) bottle.
List the different orders he could recycle the three bottles.
The first one is done for you.

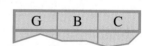

G	B	C

(b) (i) Jane has 11 green, 7 brown and 2 clear bottles to recycle.
She picks the first bottle at random. What is the probability that it is brown?
(ii) The probability that the first bottle she picks is a juice bottle is 0.4.
What is the probability that the first bottle she picks is **not** a juice bottle? OCR

2 Aimee, Georgina, Hannah and Louisa are the only runners in a race.
The probabilities of Aimee, Georgina, Hannah and Louisa winning the race are shown in the table.

Aimee	Georgina	Hannah	Louisa
0.3	0.2	0.4	

(a) Work out the probability that Louisa will win the race.
(b) Work out the probability that either Aimee or Hannah will win the race.

3 Near the end of a game of Bingo, the following numbered balls still remain in the container.

(2) (5) (8) (12) (17) (22) (23) (32) (34) (41) (42) (44)

(a) The next ball is drawn at random from the container.
What is the probability that the number will be less than 20?
(b) In fact, the next number drawn is 32. Another ball is drawn at random from the container.
What is the probability that this number will be less than 20?   OCR

4 Petra has 5 numbered cards. She uses the cards to do this experiment:

> Shuffle the cards and then record the number on the top card.

She repeats the experiment 20 times and gets these results.
    3 3 2 3 4 3 5 2 3 4 3 5 3 3 4 2 5 3 4 2
(a) What is the relative frequency of getting a 3?
(b) What numbers do you think are on the five cards? Give a reason for your answer.
(c) She repeats the experiment 500 times.
Estimate the number of times she will get a 5. Give a reason for your answer.

5 Jeff tosses a coin three times.
(a) List all the possible outcomes.
(b) What is the probability that he gets one head and two tails?

6 On Tuesday Jim has to catch a bus and a train to get to work.
The probability that the train is late is 0.4. The probability that the bus is late is 0.7.
(a) Copy and complete the tree diagram.

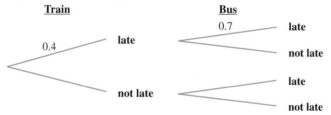

Train   **Bus**
                                        0.7 ————— **late**
              0.4 ————— **late** <
                                             ————— **not late**

                          not late < ————— **late**
                                             ————— **not late**

(b) What is the probability that both the bus and the train are late?
(c) What is the probability that either the train or the bus is late but not both?

7 (a) Bag *X* contains 3 red counters, 6 blue counters and 3 green counters.
Bag *Y* contains 4 red counters and 2 blue counters.
A bag is chosen at random and a counter is then taken from the bag.
    (i) Draw a tree diagram to show all the possible outcomes.
    (ii) What is the probability of getting a red counter?
(b) Bag *Z* contains 5 red counters and 2 green counters.
Two counters are taken from bag *Z* at random.
What is the probability of getting two counters of the same colour?

8 On his route to work, Robin drives through two sets of traffic lights.
The traffic lights operate independently.
The probability that he has to stop at the first set of lights is 0.4.
The probability that he has to stop at the second set of lights is 0.7.
(a) Find the probability that on a given day Robin stops at just one set of lights on his route to work.
(b) The operation of the traffic lights is changed so that they are NOT independent.
The probability that Robin has to stop at the first set of lights is now 0.3.
If he has to stop at the first set of lights, the probability that he has to stop at the second is 0.9
If he does not have to stop at the first set of lights, the probability that he stops at the second is 0.2.
Find the probability that on a given day Robin has to stop at just one set of lights on his route to work.   OCR

Handling Data
Non-calculator Paper

Do not use a calculator for this exercise.

1 Sylvester did a survey to find the most popular pantomime.
The results for children are shown in the table.

Pantomime	Aladdin	Cinderella	Jack and the Bean Stalk	Peter Pan
Number of children	45	35	25	15

Draw a clearly labelled pie chart to illustrate this information.

2 Two six-sided fair dice are thrown together.
The two numbers are multiplied together to give the score.

(a) Copy and complete the grid to show all possible scores.

Second dice

×	1	2	3	4	5	6
1	1	2	3	4	5	6
2	2	4	6	8	10	12
3						
4						
5						
6						

First dice

(b) What is the probability that the score is:
(i) 9, (ii) greater than 21, (iii) exactly 21?

3 The lengths of 20 bolts, in centimetres, is shown.

7.4	5.8	4.5	5.0	6.5	6.6	7.0	5.4	4.8	6.4
5.4	6.2	7.2	5.5	4.8	6.5	5.0	6.0	6.5	6.8

(a) Draw a stem and leaf diagram to show this information.
(b) What is the range in the lengths of these bolts?

4 Linzi is doing a survey to find if there should be a supermarket in her neighbourhood.
This is one of her questions.

> "Do you agree that having a supermarket in the neighbourhood would make it easier for you to do your shopping and if we did have one would you use it?"

Give two reasons why this question is unsuitable in its present form.

5 A survey is carried out about the number of road accidents in a small town.

(a) The number of accidents occurring each week for 25 weeks is recorded in the frequency table below.

Number of accidents	0	1	2	3	4	5
Number of weeks (frequency)	6	3	6	7	1	2

(i) Work out the mean number of road accidents per week.
(ii) Find the range of the number of accidents.

(b) In the next 25-week period, the mean number of accidents per week was 1.4 and the range was 7.
Make two comparisons between the number of accidents per week in the two 25-week periods.

OCR

6 Norman (N), Aled (A), Rachel (R) and Chris (C) are in the school relay team.
Norman always runs first. The order for the other three is chosen at random.

(a) Copy and complete this table to show all the possible orders for the team.

First	Second	Third	Fourth
N	A	R	C

(b) What is the probability that Rachel will run fourth?   OCR

7 Sarah recorded how far she cycled on ten of her rides and how long she took.

Distance (miles)	15	36	59	24	48	64	29	45	52	55
Time (hours)	2.2	4	7.2	3.4	6	6.9	3	5	6.5	6

(a) Draw a scatter diagram to show this information.
(b) Draw a line of best fit on your scatter diagram.
(c) (i) Another day she cycled for $4\frac{1}{2}$ hours.   ✓
    Estimate the distance she cycled.
(ii) Another day she cycled 80 miles.
    Explain why you should not use your line to estimate the time for this ride.   OCR

8 The table shows information about a group of students.

	Can speak French	Cannot speak French	
Male	5	20	25
Female	12	38	50

(a) One of these students is chosen at random.
What is the probability that the student can speak French? $\frac{17}{70}$

(b) Pru says, *"If a female student is chosen at random she is more likely to be able to
speak French than if a male student is chosen at random."*
Is she correct? Explain your answer. $\frac{12}{50} = 24\%$ $\frac{5}{25} = 20\%$

9 The graph shows the distribution of the best height jumped by each girl in a high jump
competition.

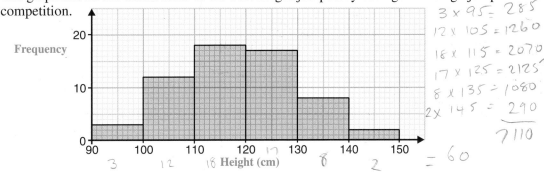

$3 \times 95 = 285$
$12 \times 105 = 1260$
$18 \times 115 = 2070$
$17 \times 125 = 2125$
$8 \times 135 = 1080$
$2 \times 145 = 290$
7110
$= 60$

3   12   18   8   2

(a) Which class interval contains the median height? $110-120$
(b) Calculate an estimate of the mean of these heights. $7110 \div 60 = 118.5\text{cm}$

10 At a fete Jessie has one go on the hoopla and one go on the darts.
The probability she wins a prize on the hoopla is 0.3.
The probability she wins a prize on the darts is 0.4.

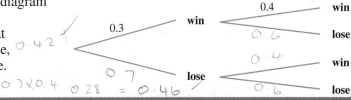

(a) Copy and complete the tree diagram
for these two events.
(b) Calculate the probability that 0.42
(i) she does not win a prize,
(ii) she wins only one prize.
$(0.3 \times 0.6)\ 0.18$ $0.7 \times 0.4\ 0.28 = 0.46$

11 Students in Year 11 were asked to write an essay on "Popstars".

  (a) The table shows the distribution of the times taken by male students to complete the essay.

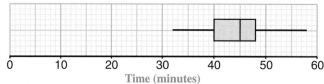

Time (t minutes)	$10 \leqslant t < 20$	$20 \leqslant t < 30$	$30 \leqslant t < 40$	$40 \leqslant t < 50$
Frequency	8	27	19	6

      (i)   Draw a cumulative frequency graph for the data.

      (ii) Use your graph to estimate the median and the interquartile range.

  (b) The box plot illustrates the distribution of the times taken by female students to complete the essay.

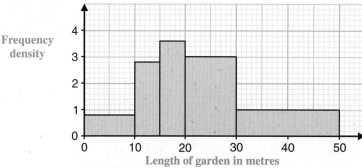

Time (minutes)

     Estimate the median and the interquartile range.

  (c) Compare and comment on the times taken by male students and the times taken by female students to complete the essay.

12 Ruben is doing a survey of the use of mobile phones among students at his school.

  (a) Give reasons why a sample of the sixth form only may be biased.

  (b) Ruben decides to take a stratified random sample of 10% of all the students in the school.

      (i)   Describe how he chooses his sample.

      (ii) Give one advantage this method has over a simple random sample.

13 The weather forecast for London gives a 60% chance of a shower, and for Brighton gives a 70% chance of a shower.

  (a) Find the probability of showers falling in either London or Brighton but not both.

  (b) What assumption is made in this calculation?

             OCR

14 A survey was carried out to find the average length of a garden.
The histogram shows the results.

Frequency density

Length of garden in metres

  (a) How many gardens were included in the survey?

  (b) Use the histogram to estimate:

      (i)   the percentage of gardens less than 12 metres in length,

      (ii) the median length of a garden.

15 A new machine contains a rod and a cam. Both these parts may rattle.
The probability that the rod rattles is 0.7.
If the rod rattles, then the probability that the cam rattles is 0.4.
If the rod does not rattle, then the probability that the cam rattles is 0.2.

  (a) Find the probability that

      (i)   both rod and cam rattle,   (ii) exactly one of these two parts rattles.

  (b) The machine also contains a pump.
     The probability that this rattles is independent of the other parts rattling.
     The probability that none of the three parts rattles is 0.024.
     Find the probability that the pump does not rattle.

             OCR

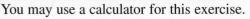
Section Review

You may use a calculator for this exercise.

1 Karina is playing a game with these cards. | X | Y | 1 | 1 | 3 |

One card is taken at random from the letters.
One card is taken at random from the numbers.
(a)   List all the possible outcomes.
(b)   Explain why the probability of getting | X | 1 | is not $\frac{1}{4}$.

2 A box contains 20 plastic ducks.
3 of the ducks are green, 10 are blue and the rest are yellow.
A duck is taken from the box at random.
What is the probability that it is: (a)   green,   (b)   yellow?

3 Tom asked students in his school how they spent last Saturday morning.
The table shows the results for 200 year 11 students.

	Paid job	Doing homework	In bed	Sport	Other
Number of students	72	24	50	46	8

(a)   Draw a pie chart to show Tom's results for the year 11 students.

This pie chart shows Tom's results for the year 13 students.
(b)   (i)   State one way in which the results for
years 11 and 13 are similar.
(ii)   State one way in which the results for
years 11 and 13 are different.

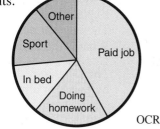

OCR

4 The mean weight of the 16 girls in a class is 55.4 kg.
The mean weight of the 14 boys in the class is 58.2 kg.
Calculate the mean weight of the 30 pupils in the class.

OCR

5 Tariq and James collect data on the number of people in each car passing their school
at lunchtime.
(a)   Tariq presented the data collected on Monday in the following table.

Number of people in a car	1	2	3	4	5
Number of cars	21	17	9	2	1

(i)   Find the median number of people in a car.
(ii)   Calculate the mean number of people in a car.
(b)   James is collecting his data on Tuesday. He says, "Based on the data I've collected so
far, the probability that the next car will contain just one person is 0.25."
(i)   What is the probability that the next car will contain more than one person?
(ii)   James has recorded 48 cars in his survey.
How many cars contained just one person?

OCR

6 Last Friday, a supermarket pizza stand sold the following numbers of pizzas.

Cheese & Tomato 125,   Ham & Pineapple 96,   Triple Cheese 87,   Pepperoni 12

Next Friday, the supermarket expects to sell 240 pizzas in total.
Use the figures from last Friday to estimate the number of Ham & Pineapple pizzas they
should make.

OCR

111

7 The engine size and distance travelled on one litre of petrol for each of 10 cars is summarised in the table below.

Engine size (litres)	0.6	1	1	1.1	1.6	1.8	2	2.5	2.5	3
Distance (km)	12	12	11	10	8	8	7	6	10	4

(a) Draw a scatter diagram to illustrate this information.
(b) One of these cars had been fitted with a new, efficient engine.
Identify this car by circling a point on the scatter diagram.
(c) Describe the type and the strength of the correlation shown in your diagram.
(d) (i) Draw a line of best fit on your diagram.
    (ii) Estimate the distance covered by a car with a 1.3 litre engine.   OCR

8 Jenni recorded the time of each of the tracks in her CD collection.
Her results are summarised below.

Time (t seconds)	Number of tracks
$120 < t \leq 150$	13
$150 < t \leq 180$	9
$180 < t \leq 210$	8
$210 < t \leq 240$	7
$240 < t \leq 270$	3

(a) Calculate an estimate of the mean time.
(b) Which class contains the median?
Explain how you found your answer.
(c) The random play on Jenni's CD player selects a track.
What is the probability it will last more than 240 seconds?   OCR

9 (a) The frequency distribution table gives information about the distances travelled to school by pupils at a primary school.

Distance (k kilometres)	Frequency
$0 \leq k < 1$	36
$1 \leq k < 2$	76
$2 \leq k < 3$	28
$3 \leq k < 4$	12
$4 \leq k < 5$	8

  (i) Draw a cumulative frequency graph to illustrate the data.
  (ii) Use your graph to find the median and the interquartile range.
(b) A survey of the distances travelled to school by pupils at a secondary school gave the following information.

Shortest distance	0.2 km	Median	2.8 km
Longest distance	9.6 km	Lower quartile	2.0 km
		Upper quartile	3.4 km

Draw a box plot to illustrate the data.
(c) Compare and comment on the distances travelled to school by pupils at these schools.

10 Here is a list of the last 8 quarterly gas bills for a householder.

Month	Jan.	Apr.	Jul.	Oct.	Jan.	Apr.	Jul.	Oct.
Amount	£67	£188	£27	£18	£139	£103	£23	£27

Calculate the first two 4-point moving averages for this data.

11 James and Simon take their driving test on the same day.
The probability that James will pass is 0.8.
The probability that Simon will pass is 0.7.
These events are independent.
  (a)   Draw a tree diagram to show all the possible outcomes of the two tests.
        Label the diagram carefully.
  (b)   Calculate the probability that only one of them passes the test.   OCR

12 Martin is playing with a biased, four-sided dice. The four faces are numbered 1, 2, 3 and 4.
When Martin throws the dice, his score is the number it lands on.
The table shows the probability of his scoring 1, 2 or 3.

Score	1	2	3
Probability	0.4	0.15	0.25

  (a)   Martin throws the dice once.
        What is the probability that he scores   (i)   4,   (ii)   2 or 3?
  (b)   Martin throws the dice twice.
        Find the probability that he scores
        (i)   3 on each throw,
        (ii)   a total of 3 on the two throws.   OCR

13 The table shows the distribution of the times, in minutes, that people had to wait for their meals at a restaurant.

Time (t minutes)	$0 \leqslant t < 10$	$10 \leqslant t < 15$	$15 \leqslant t < 25$	$25 \leqslant t < 40$
Frequency	25	21	24	9

  (a)   Draw a histogram to represent these waiting times.
  (b)   Estimate the median waiting time.
  (c)   Estimate how many people had to wait more than 30 minutes for their meal.

14 The table shows the age distribution of employees in a large factory.

Age in years (y)	Number of employees
$16 \leqslant y < 25$	300
$25 \leqslant y < 40$	447
$40 \leqslant y < 60$	375
$60 \leqslant y < 65$	228
Total	1350

The company directors want to make a change in working hours.
They decide to send out a questionnaire to 100 of the employees.
  (a)   Calculate how many employees from each age group are needed to make a
        stratified sample.
  (b)   State **one** advantage of using a stratified sample rather than a simple random sample.
                                                                                      OCR

15 Judy has to go through two sets of traffic lights on her way to work.
The probability that she has to stop at the first set of traffic lights is $\frac{2}{5}$.
If she stops at the first set of traffic lights, the probability that she has to stop at the
second set is $\frac{3}{4}$.
If she does not stop at the first set of traffic lights, the probability that she has to stop at the
second set is $\frac{1}{10}$.
On any particular day, what is the probability that
  (a)   she has to stop at just one set of lights on her way to work,
  (b)   she has to stop at least once at the traffic lights on her way to work?   OCR

Do not use a calculator for this exercise.

1 (a) Given that $2065 \div 59 = 35$, find the exact value of: $20\,650 \div 5.9$.
(b) Use approximations to estimate the value of 49×302. Show all your working.

2 A is the point $(-4, -1)$. B is the point $(2, 3)$. What is the midpoint of the line segment AB?

3 Solve the equations (a) $3a - 2 = -5$, (b) $5m + 3 = 7 - m$, (c) $3(a - 2) = 6$.

4 A packet contains 1 red balloon, 3 white balloons and 4 blue balloons.
A balloon is taken from the packet at random.
What is the probability that it is (a) red, (b) red or white, (c) not white?

5 Here is part of the timetable for the Swanage railway.

Norden (N)	10:30
Corfe Castle (C)	10:32
Harman's Cross (H)	10:41
Swanage (S)	10:53

Here are the distances between the stations.

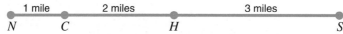

(a) Draw a distance-time graph for this journey.
(b) Mark with an arrow the section of the graph that shows when the train was travelling fastest.
(c) Explain one way in which your graph does not show exactly how the train is really travelling.
OCR

6 A cuboid has a volume of $90\,\text{cm}^3$. The base of the cuboid measures $3\,\text{cm}$ by $6\,\text{cm}$.
Calculate the height of the cuboid.

7 (a) Work out. $\frac{3}{5} + \frac{1}{4}$
(b) Beth and Lucy share £80 in the ratio 3 : 1. Work out how much each of them receives.
OCR

8 The numbers on these cards are coded. The sum of the numbers on these 3 cards is 41.

x	$2x - 1$	$3x$

(a) Form an equation in x.
(b) By solving your equation, find the numbers on the cards.

9 (a) In the diagram the lines AB and CD are parallel.
They are crossed by two straight lines.
Find angle x, giving a reason for your answer.

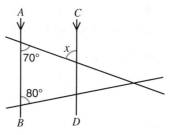

(b)

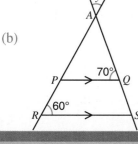

In this diagram, the lines PQ and RS are parallel.
Find angle y, showing how you obtained your answer.
OCR

10 A sequence begins: 2, 5, 8, 11, …
Write in terms of n, the nth term of the sequence.

11 The diagram shows the positions of shapes P, Q and R.

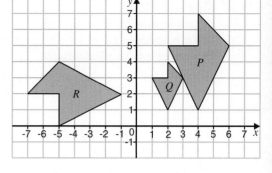

  (a) Describe fully the single transformation which takes:
      (i) P onto Q,   (ii) P onto R.
  (b) Copy shape Q onto squared paper and draw an enlargement of the shape with scale factor -2, centre $(0, 3)$.

12 (a) Jack's foot length is 20 cm.
      His height is 1.6 m.
      Write, in the form $1 : n$, the ratio: Jack's foot length : Jack's height
  (b) Janet's foot length and height are in the same ratio as Jack's.
      Her foot length is 14 cm. Work out her height.
  (c) Jagdeep's foot length is 21 cm, correct to the nearest centimetre.
      Write down his greatest and least possible foot length.   OCR

13 Cocoa is sold in cylindrical tins. The height of a tin is 7.9 cm. The radius of a tin is 4.1 cm.
Use approximations to estimate the volume of a tin. Show all your working.

14 (a) Factorise. $6x + 15$
  (b) Solve this equation. $3(x - 7) = x - 4$ OCR

15 ABC is a triangular field. $AB = 100$ m, $BC = 85$ m and $AC = 115$ m.
  (a) Construct a plan of the field using a scale of 1 cm to 10 m.
  (b) A mobile phone company plans to erect a mast in the field.
      The mast must be exactly the same distance from A as it is from B.
      The mast must also be closer to AB than it is to BC.
      Indicate, on your plan, all possible positions for the mast.   OCR

16 These formulae represent quantities connected with containers, where a, b and c are dimensions.
$$2(ab + bc + cd) \qquad abc \qquad \sqrt{a^2 + b^2} \qquad 4(a + b + c)$$
Which of these formulae represent lengths? Explain how you know.

17 Work out. $(6.9 \times 10^{12}) \div (3 \times 10^5)$. Give your answer in standard form.   OCR

18 (a) Multiply out and simplify. $(x - 5)(x + 6)$
  (b) (i) Factorise. $x^2 - 10x + 24$
      (ii) Hence, simplify. $\dfrac{x^2 - 10x + 24}{x^2 - 16}$ OCR

19 You are given the formula $a = bc^2$.
  (a) Calculate the value of a when $b = 100$ and $c = -\frac{3}{5}$.
  (b) Rearrange the formula to give c in terms of a and b.

20 (a) Copy and complete the table for the equation $y = x^2 - 3x - 2$.

x	-1	0	1	2	3	4
y			-4	-4	-2	

  (b) Hence, draw the graph of $y = x^2 - 3x - 2$.
  (c) Use your graph to find the smallest value of y.
  (d) Use your graph to find the solutions of the equation $x^2 - 3x - 2 = 0$.
  (e) By drawing a suitable straight line on your graph, find the solutions of the equation $x^2 - 4x - 2 = 0$.   OCR

21 In the diagram, $ABCD$ is a cyclic quadrilateral.
CDE is a straight line.

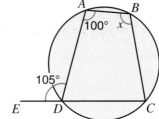

(a) Find angle x.
Give a reason for your answer.

(b) Is AB parallel to EC?
Give a reason for your answer.

OCR

22 (a) Simplify as far as possible (i) $\dfrac{12p^2q}{3p} \times 2q^2$. (ii) $\dfrac{12x - 4y}{4}$.

(b) Work out, as a **fraction**, the exact value of $\left(\dfrac{49}{4}\right)^{\frac{-3}{2}}$.

OCR

23 The sketches show the graphs of four equations. Write down the equation for each graph.

(a) 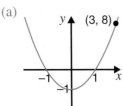 (b) 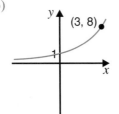 (c) 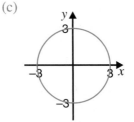 (d)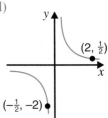

24 In triangle RST, A and B are the midpoints of RS and RT respectively.
$\overrightarrow{RS} = x$ and $\overrightarrow{RT} = y$.

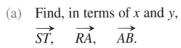

(a) Find, in terms of x and y,

$\overrightarrow{ST}, \quad \overrightarrow{RA}, \quad \overrightarrow{AB}$.

(b) What conclusions can you draw about the lines AB and ST?

OCR

25 (a) Show that $(n - 3)^2 - 2(n - 3) = (n - 3)(n - 5)$.

(b) Solve the equation $x^2 + 3x - 10 = 0$.

26 (a) Rationalise the denominator of $\dfrac{2}{\sqrt{5}}$.

(b) When $p = \sqrt{2}$ and $q = \sqrt{6}$, write pq in the form $a\sqrt{b}$ where a and b are integers
and b is as small as possible.

OCR

27 (a) Simplify. $\dfrac{4x^2 - 6x}{2x^2 + 3x - 9}$

(b) Rearrange the formula $p = \dfrac{mn}{m + n}$ to give m in terms of p and n.

(c) Solve the simultaneous equations $x + 2y = 5$ and $x = \dfrac{2}{y}$.

28 (a) Sketch the graph of $y = \cos x°$ for $0° \leqslant x \leqslant 360°$.

(b) Use the graph to solve these equations for $0° \leqslant x \leqslant 360°$.

(i) $\cos x° = -0.4$ (ii) $4 \cos x° = 3$

OCR

29 (a) It is given that $N = 0.\overset{..}{5}\overset{..}{7}$. Show that $99N = 57$.

(b) Hence, express $0.0\overset{..}{5}\overset{..}{7}$ as a fraction in its lowest terms.

OCR

30 A committee has 7 male members and 5 female members.
Two members of the committee are chosen at random to attend a conference.
What is the probability that both members are of the same sex?

31 (a) Draw the graph of $y = 2^x$ for values of x from -2 to 4.

(b) Use your graph to find

(i) $2^{2.3}$, (ii) the solution to the equation $2^x - 3 = 11$.

OCR

Calculator Paper ●●●●●●●●●●●●●●●

You may use a calculator for this exercise.

1 (a) Write $\frac{7}{9}$ as a decimal. Give your answer correct to two decimal places.

  (b) Write 33%, 0.3, $\frac{8}{25}$ and $\frac{1}{3}$ in order of size, smallest first.

2 A recipe for a fruit crumble includes these ingredients.

| 200 g flour | 125 g margarine | 100 g sugar | 20 g ginger | 750 g rhubarb |

  (a) Paul has 300 g of flour. He uses it all to make a larger fruit crumble with the recipe. What weight of sugar should he use?

  (b) Sally has 600 g of rhubarb. She uses it to make a smaller crumble with the recipe. What weight of margarine should she use?   OCR

3 (a) A regular polygon has 9 sides. Work out the sum of its interior angles.

  (b) In the diagram, *PQ* is parallel to *RS*. Find the size of angles *a*, *b* and *c*.

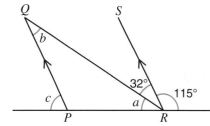

4 (a) Multiply out and simplify where possible.
    (i) $x(x - 3)$ (ii) $5(2y + 1) + 3y$

  (b) Factorise. (i) $6a + 9$ (ii) $2b^2 + b$

  (c) Solve. (i) $\frac{x}{5} = 20$ (ii) $4x + 3 = 2x - 6$ OCR

5 A hang glider flies 2.8 km on a bearing of 070° from *P* to *Q* and then 2 km on a bearing of 200° from *Q* to *R*.

  (a) Make a scale drawing to show the flight of the hang glider from *P* to *Q* to *R*. Use a scale of 1 cm to 200 m.

  (b) From *R* the hang glider flies directly back to *P*. Use your drawing to find the distance and bearing of *P* from *R*.

6 A bill for a meal for six people was £128.40. The bill included £34.68 for drinks. What percentage of the bill was for drinks?   OCR

7 The table shows the weight of the luggage for passengers on one plane.

Weight (*w* kg)	$0 < w \leqslant 5$	$5 < w \leqslant 10$	$10 < w \leqslant 15$	$15 < w \leqslant 20$	$20 < w \leqslant 25$
Number of passengers	14	28	12	9	2

  (a) What was the modal class?

  (b) One of the passengers is selected at random. What is the probability that this passenger's luggage weighs 15 kg or less?

  (c) Draw a frequency diagram for this distribution.

  (d) Calculate an estimate of the mean weight of luggage for these passengers.   OCR

8 The diagram shows a solid triangular prism made of metal. The triangle has base 4.2 cm and height 3.5 cm.

  (a) Find the area of the triangle.

  (b) The length of the prism is 9.8 cm. Find the volume of the prism.

  (c) The mass of the prism is 500 g. What is the density of the metal?   OCR

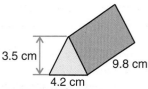

9 Use a trial and improvement method to find a solution to the equation $x^3 + x = 57$.
Show all your working and give your answer correct to one decimal place.

10 The diagram shows a semi-circle with diameter AB.
C is a point on the circumference.
$\angle ACB = 90°$. $AC = 6\,\text{cm}$ and $CB = 8\,\text{cm}$.
Calculate the area of the shaded triangle
as a percentage of the area of the semi-circle.

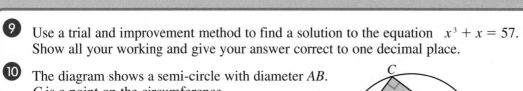

11 A biased, six-sided dice has a probability of $\frac{3}{8}$ of landing on a 6.
The dice is thrown 500 times.
About how many times would you expect it **not** to land on 6?

OCR

12 (a) Write down the values of n, where n is an integer, which satisfies the inequality
$$-1 < n + 2 \leqslant 3.$$
(b) Solve the inequality $2x + 3 < 4$.

13 The Earth is 150 000 000 km from the Sun.
(a) Write this distance in standard form.
(b) The Earth is 3.81×10^5 km from the Moon.
How many times greater is the distance of the Earth from the Sun than its distance from the Moon?
(c) Saturn is 1.4×10^9 km from the Sun.

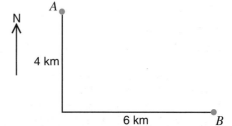

The Sun, Earth and Saturn are sometimes in a straight line, as shown.
Calculate the distance between the Earth and Saturn when this happens.

OCR

14 The diagram shows the position of two radio masts, A and B.
B is 4 km south and 6 km east of A.
(a) Calculate the distance from A to B.
(b) Calculate the bearing of B from A.

OCR

15 Solve. (a) $6(x + 3) = 2x + 28$ (b) $2x + y = 9$
$3x - y = 16$

OCR

16 (a) Maria invested £2000 for 3 years at 2.7% per annum compound interest.
How much was her investment worth at the end of 3 years?
(b) Maria used some of the money to buy a dress in a sale.
The price of the dress had been reduced by 35% to the sale price of £37.70.
What was the price of the dress before the sale?

OCR

17 The mass of a solid sphere is directly proportional to the cube of its radius.
A sphere with radius 1.2 cm has mass 21.6 g.
Calculate the radius of a sphere of the same material with mass 34.3 g.

OCR

18 The length of a rectangle is y cm.
The perimeter of this rectangle is 30 cm.
The area of this rectangle is 55 cm².
(a) Form an equation in y and show that it can be simplified to $y^2 - 15y + 55 = 0$.
(b) Solve the equation $y^2 - 15y + 55 = 0$ to find the length and width of the rectangle.
Give your answers correct to 2 decimal places.

OCR

19 A maths student did an experiment in which she hung various masses on a coiled spring. For each mass, m grams, she measured the total length, l centimetres, of the spring. The table shows her results.

Mass (m grams)	10	20	30	40	50	75	100
Length (l cm)	3.2	4.4	5.5	6.2	7.2	9.8	12

(a) She thinks that m and l are connected by the equation $l = am + b$, where a and b are constants. Plot a scatter graph for her results and draw the line of best fit. Use it to find the values of a and b.

(b) What does the value of b tell you about the spring?

(c) Estimate the length of the spring when a mass of 135 g is hung on it. State any assumption that you make.

OCR

20 A standard ice cream cone has diameter 5 cm and height 10 cm.

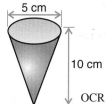

(a) Ice cream is put into a standard cone until it is filled level with the top. What volume of ice cream does the cone contain?

(b) A super cone is mathematically similar to a standard cone and contains 30% more ice cream. What is the height of the super cone to the nearest centimetre?

OCR

21 (a) Remove the brackets and write as simply as possible $(3x - 5y)(2x + y)$.

(b) Factorise the expression $4a^2b + ab^2$.

(c) Make r the subject of the formula $y = \dfrac{2(r + h)}{(r - h)}$.

OCR

22 This table summarises the prices of 100 houses advertised for sale in a newspaper.

Price £C (thousands)	$50 \leqslant C < 150$	$150 \leqslant C < 250$	$250 \leqslant C < 500$	$500 \leqslant C < 1000$
Number of houses	23	32	40	5

Draw a histogram to show these data.

OCR

23 (a) $x^2 + 8x - 24$ can be written in the form $(x + a)^2 - b$. Find the values of a and b.

(b) State the minimum value of $y = x^2 + 8x - 24$.

(c) Solve the equation $x^2 + 8x - 24 = 0$.

OCR

24 A very small island, A, is on the bearing of $036°$ from a port, P, on the mainland. A fishing boat at B is on a bearing of $070°$ from A. The boat is 9.7 km from A and 21.3 km from P. Calculate the bearing of B from P.

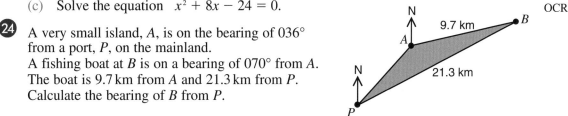

OCR

25 Prove that this is true for all values of x. $(x + 1)^2 - (x^2 + 1) = 2x$

OCR
OCR

26 In the table below, x and y are connected by an equation of the form $y = kx^n$.

x	2	4	6	p
y	12	48	108	147

(a) Find the values of k and n.   (b) Find the value of p.

OCR

27 Solve, algebraically, these simultaneous equations. $x + y = 5$
$$x^2 + 3y^2 = 49$$

OCR

28

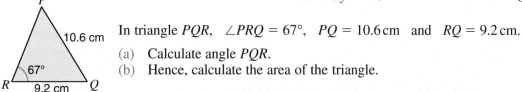

In triangle PQR, $\angle PRQ = 67°$, $PQ = 10.6$ cm and $RQ = 9.2$ cm.

(a) Calculate angle PQR.

(b) Hence, calculate the area of the triangle.

Answers

Exercise 1   Page 1

1. (a) 1 005 010   (b) 23 500
2. (a) 10 070   (b) 6685
   (c) 100 147   (d) 154
3. (a) (i) 9623   (ii) 2396   (b) 7227
4. £181 per month
5. £3072
6. (a) 295   (b) 11 676
7. 21
8. (a) 8   (b) 4   (c) 105   (d) 2
9. 7
10. 125 girls
11. 115 cm
12. £6894
13. (a) 800 000   (b) 14.5
14. $-4°$F
15. (a) -7 (b) -3 (c) -6
16. 5
17. 98 304
18. £20 563 720

Exercise 2   Page 3

1. (a) There are two figures after the decimal
   points in the question but only one in
   the answer.
   (b) (i) 0.12   (ii) 0.06
2. £229.12
3. 1.57 m
4. £2.50 per kilogram
5. (a) 7.36   (b) 3.2   (c) 230
6. $0 < m < 1$. E.g. $\frac{1}{2}$, $\frac{2}{5}$
7. (a) $\frac{5}{12}$ (b) $\frac{2}{3}$
8. (a) $\frac{2}{3}$ (b) $\frac{3}{14}$
9. £46
10. £3.92 per kilogram
11. (a) $1\frac{5}{12}$ (b) $\frac{9}{10}$
12. $\frac{13}{60}$
13. (a) $1\frac{7}{15}$ (b) 2
14. $\frac{12}{25}$
15. $\frac{9}{20}$
16. (a) 0.1875   (b) $\frac{6}{11}$
17. £120
18. 17.76792453

Exercise 3   Page 5

1. (a) 630   (b) 626.5   (c) 600
2. 19 500
3. $\frac{3000 \times 40}{100} = £1200$
4. (a) £60 000 ÷ 20 = £3000
   (b) $\frac{50 \times 40}{0.5} = \frac{2000}{0.5} = 4000$
5. (a) $40 \times £7$
   (b) Bigger. 40 is bigger than 39, and
   £7 is bigger than £6.95.
6. 644
7. (a) $\frac{9000}{10} \times 90p = £810$
   (b) 9000 is larger than 8873,
   10 is smaller than 11, and
   90 is larger than 89.9.
8. No. For example, an answer of 0.01634…
   is 0.02 to 2 d.p. and 0.016 to 2 s.f.
   0.016 is more accurate.
9. (a) 8.299 492 386   (b) 8.30
10. 6.4
11. (a) 0.3   (b) $\frac{50 - 20}{30 + 60} = \frac{30}{90} \approx 0.3$
12. Lower bound 9.1 kg, upper bound 9.3 kg.
13. $m = \frac{13.95}{8.55} \approx 1.63158$

Exercise 4   Page 7

1. 8%   10. £21.25
2. 28 marks   11. £22 035
3. £40.80   12. 14 230 cm³
4. £5.20   13. (a) 40%   (b) £960
5. 39 hours   14. (a) £96   (b) £210
6. £480   15. 32%
7. £46.75   16. 400
8. Small bar.   17. £9272.88
   Large: 2.66 g/p   18. (a) £3472.88
   Small: 2.78 g/p   (b) 19.1%
9. 81

Exercise 5   Page 10

1. (a) 1, 2, 3, 6, 9, 18   (b) 35
   (c) 15 has more than 2 factors: 1, 3, 5, 15
2. (a) 16   (b) 125
   (c) 10 000   (d) 2 500 000
3. (a) 27   (b) 16   (c) 0.09   (d) 80
4. No. $1^3 + 2^3 = 1 + 8 = 9$ $3^3 = 27$

5. For example: $2^2 + 3^2 = 13$ and $3^2 + 5^2 = 34$

6. (a) 55   (b) 8100   (c) 200

7. (a) (i) 1000   (ii) 2   (iii) 0.36
    (b) (i) 27   (ii) 23 or 29

8. (a) 72   (b) 17   (c) 112

9. (a) 7^{-1} $\left(\text{or } \frac{1}{7}\right)$ (b) 13   (c) $2^3 \times 3 \times 5$

10. (a) $2^2 \times 3^2$ (b) $3^2 \times 5$
    (c) 9   (d) 180

11. 4

12. 30 seconds

13. (a) 12   (b) 225   (c) 32

14. (a) $\sqrt{225}$, $\sqrt{225} = 15$, $2^4 = 16$
    (b) $2\frac{1}{3}$

15. (a) $x = 9$ (b) $x = 3$
    (c) $x = 18$ (d) $x = 1$

16. (a) 3^5 (b) 4^3 (c) 5^3 (d) 9^6 (e) 2^{-2}

17. (a) 6400
    (b) (i) $n = -4$ (ii) $n = 0$ (iii) $n = -2$

18. (a) 3   (b) $\frac{1}{8}$ (c) 125   (d) $\frac{1}{8}$

19. (a) $\frac{9}{25}$

20. (a) $\frac{8}{5}$ (b) $\frac{1}{9}$ (c) $\frac{8}{25}$

21. (a) 0.14   (b) 175.616

22. 6.76

23. (a) 3.27   (b) 9.6

24. 3.465

25. (a) 10.657
    (b) $\sqrt{\dfrac{4}{0.2^2}} = \sqrt{\dfrac{4}{0.04}} = \sqrt{100} = 10$

26. (a) 1.9   (b) 5.9   (c) 11   (d) 0.073

SECTION 6

Exercise 6   Page 12

1. 1×10^6

2. Largest: 13 100, smallest: 0.0057

3. (a) 5.7×10^7 (b) 5.7×10^{-5}

4. (a) 92 000 000   (b) 3.05×10^{-1}

5. (a) 1.3×10^{-4} (b) 31 400 000
    (c) 1.5×10^4

6. (a) 5.6×10^4 (b) 3×10^8
    (c) 1.2×10^{-1}

7. (a) Mexico   (b) 4 700 000
    (c) 1.271×10^8

8. (a) 12.5 km $\leqslant$ diameter $<$ 13.5 km
    (b) 2.28×10^8 (c) 500 seconds

9. (a) 6×10^{-6} (b) 6×10^8

10. 4.329×10^5 kg

11. (a) 1.6×10^9 (b) 0.000 79

12. 11.1 light years

13. 0.000 008 5

14. 0.007

15. (a) 4×10^{-4} (b) 9.8×10^{11}

SECTION 7

Exercise 7   Page 14

1. 8 large bricks
2. 75%
3. £25
4. 4 : 1
5. £87
6. (a) 70%
    (b) 9 women
7. (a) 150 g
    (b) 100 ml
8. £1.96
9. £517.50
10. (a) £24
    (b) Emma: £54
       Rebecca: £36
11. 4 days
12. £32.40
13. 1 : 20 000
14. £930
15. 48 minutes

SECTION 8

Exercise 8   Page 16

1. $1\frac{1}{2}$ hours
2. 165 km
3. 48 miles per hour
4. 3.6 km/h
5. (a) 60 mph
    (b) 190 miles
6. (a) 40 mph
    (b) 1116
7. 47 mph
8. Yes
    $\frac{65}{80} \times 60 = 48.75$ mins
    Arrives 1029
9. 1.8 km
10. 28.8 mph
11. (a) $1\frac{1}{2}$ hours
     (b) 50 mph
12. 22.5 km/h
13. 10 m/s
14. 1.27 seconds
15. (a) 12 seconds
     (b) 127.8 km/h
16. 9 g/cm^3
17. 19 g
18. 259.3 people/km^2

SECTION 9

Exercise 9   Page 19

1. (a) $0.\dot{7}1428\dot{5}$ (b) $\frac{2}{9}$

2. (a) 4   (b) 25

3. (a) $5\sqrt{5}$ (b) 3   (c) 6   (d) $\frac{3}{4}$

4. (a) $100 \times 0.4\dot{5} = 45.4\dot{5}$
      $99 \times 0.4\dot{5} = 45.4\dot{5} - 0.4\dot{5} = 45$
      So, $0.4\dot{5} = \frac{45}{99} = \frac{5}{11}$
    (b) $\frac{7}{11}$

5. $\frac{4}{11}$

6. (a) $2 \times 2 \times 3 = 2^2 \times 3$
    (b) $a = 2$, $b = 3$

7. (a) $3\sqrt{5}$ (b) $5\sqrt{3}$

8. $3\sqrt{2}$

9. (a) (i) $10\sqrt{5}$ (ii) $5\sqrt{2}$ (iii) $10\sqrt{30}$
    (b) (i) $\frac{\sqrt{5}}{5}$ (ii) $4\sqrt{3}$

10. (a) $4\sqrt{3}$ (b) 9   (c) $\sqrt{3}$ (d) 30

11. $12\sqrt{3}$

121

12. (a) $2\sqrt{3}$ (b) $\frac{3\sqrt{5}}{2}$

13. (a) $k = 5$ (b) $6\sqrt{3}$

14. (a) 30 (b) $a = 21$, $b = 6$

15. (a) $5 - 2\sqrt{5}$ (b) $14 + 6\sqrt{5}$
 (c) $-9 - 7\sqrt{5}$

16. (a) $n = 20$ (b) $-1\frac{1}{2}$

Number

Non-calculator Paper   Page 20

1. (a) 3 is a factor of 15 and 27. (b) 27
 (c) (i) 15 and 27 (more than 2 factors).
  (ii) 35

2. (a) (i) 4.74 (ii) 0.08 (iii) 80
 (b) £23.40

3. (a) $\frac{1}{2}$, $\frac{3}{5}$, $\frac{5}{8}$, $\frac{2}{3}$, $\frac{3}{4}$ (b) $\frac{9}{40}$
 (c) (i) $\frac{13}{20}$ (ii) $\frac{1}{6}$ (iii) $\frac{8}{15}$

4. $50 \times £10 + 100 \times £7 + 30 \times £15$
 $= £500 + £700 + £450 = £1650$
 He does not have enough money.

5. (a) 16 km/h (b) 1106

6. (a) (i) 586 740 (ii) 0.462
 (b) $\frac{3000}{50 \times 20} = \frac{3000}{1000} = 3$

7. (a) (i) 4 (ii) 10 (b) $4\frac{5}{12}$

8. (a) 200 (b) $2 \times 3 \times 5$

9. (a) Blackberries. Same reduction in price
 from a smaller amount.
 (b) 120 grams (c) 20% (d) 8.5 kg

10. 10

11. (a) (i) $2^4 \times 3$ (ii) $2^2 \times 3^3$ (b) 432

12. (a) (i) 1 (ii) $\frac{1}{36}$ (iii) 8
 (b) 3^2 (c) 9.4×10^{-5} (d) 382 000

13. 40

14. 176 cm

15. (a) $3\frac{1}{3}$ (b) $1\frac{1}{2}$

16. 60 pence

17. 80 km/h

18. 20 male passengers

19. (a) 3×10^4 (b) (i) $2\sqrt{2}$ (ii) $\sqrt{2}$

20. (a) $2^4 \times 3 \times 5$ (b) 15

21. 9 minutes

22. (a) 36 (b) $\frac{1}{7}$ (c) -1

23. (a) 0.4 (b) $\left(\frac{1}{4}\right)^{\frac{1}{2}}$, $\left(\frac{1}{2}\right)^2$, 5^{-1}, 2^{-3}, 3^{-2}
 (c) (i) $x = 7$ (ii) $x = 2$ (iii) $x = 1$

24. Lower bound = 4.55 litres
 Upper bound = 4.65 litres

25. (a) (i) $8\sqrt{3}$ (ii) 4
 (b) 16 (c) $\frac{1}{3}$ (d) $\frac{7}{33}$

Number

Calculator Paper   Page 22

1. 24.1 kg

2. (a) (i) 52.037 (ii) 52.04 (iii) 52.0
 (b) (i) 6.7 (ii) 8.41 (iii) 65 (iv) $3.\dot{3}$

3. (a) 200 g (b) 30 (c) 13 pence

4. (a) 4 : 3 (b) 60.7% (c) £2.10

5. Small.
 Small: $\frac{180}{36} = 5$ g/p Large: $\frac{300}{63} = 4.76$ g/p

6. 0.5 litres

7. 68 mph

8. £115.15

9. (a) 16.4 (b) 0.08, 11%, $\frac{9}{20}$, 0.7
 (c) £2.10 per kg

10. £144

11. 12.5%

12. (a) (i) 290 (ii) $\frac{600 \times 30}{80 - 20} = \frac{18\,000}{60} = 300$
 (b) 4

13. (a) £352 (b) 1150 litres

14. (a) 0.625 (b) 63.125

15. (a) £6324 (b) 8.4%

16. Numbers between 0 and 1.

17. 32 minutes

18. Yes. 5×75.5 kg $= 377.5$ kg

19. $\sqrt{6.9}$, 2.58, $2\frac{4}{7}$, 1.6^2

20. 12%

21. (a) (i) $\frac{2}{3}$ (ii) 0.025 (b) 8.75×10^{-3}

22. 7290 million

23. (a) 7.65×10^{-4} (b) 9.7×10^8

24. 3150

25. 126.3 people per square kilometre

26. (a) 7.5 million tonnes (b) 0924

27. (a) 1.728×10^7 (b) 1.85

28. (a) £2415.90 (b) £1200

29. £27 385

30. 360 books

31. 0.41%

32. (a) $3\sqrt{5}$ (b) $\frac{\sqrt{10}}{2}$ (c) $2^{\frac{5}{2}}$ (d) $1\frac{5}{16}$ (e) $\frac{3}{11}$

33. £8500

34. 3.9×10^{-2}

35. (a) $-60 + 37\sqrt{3}$ (b) (i) $5\sqrt{2}$ (ii) $2\sqrt{2}$

SECTION   10

Exercise 10   Page 25

1. (a) $(t + 5)$ years (b) $(x - 5)$ years

2. $(3x + 2y)$ pence

3. (a) $6m$ (b) $m + 2$ (c) m^3

4. $(4x + 200)$ degrees

5. $(5d + 15)$ pence

6. $\boxed{a + a}$ and $\boxed{2a}$ $\boxed{2(a + 1)}$ and $\boxed{2a + 2}$
 $\boxed{2a + 1}$ and $\boxed{a + a + 1}$ $\boxed{a^2}$ and $\boxed{a \times a}$

7. (a) (i) $3x + 3$ (ii) $x + 2y$
   (b) (i) $2x + 6$ (ii) $x^2 - x$
   (c) (i) $2x - 5$ (ii) $13 + 3x$
   (d) (i) $2(a - 3)$ (ii) $x(x + 2)$

8. (a) $p + 6t + 16$ (b) $6p - 10t$

9. (a) $3ab - 2a - b$ (b) $8x + 19$

10. $(500 - 6x)$ pence

11. (a) $12 - x$ (b) $(d + 5)$ pence
   (c) $x(d + 5) + d(12 - x) = (5x + 12d)$ pence

12. (a) y^5 (b) x^3 (c) z^2 (d) $\dfrac{x}{y}$

13. $3x(5x + 3y)$

14. (a) $8 - 6n$ (b) $6m^2$ (c) $2m(4n - 1)$

15. $4x - 1$

16. (a) (i) $6a^4$ (ii) $2x^6$ (iii) $2mn^4$ (iv) $20x^5y^2$
   (b) (i) $9m^6$ (ii) $8a^6b^3$

17. (a) (i) $2x^2 - 6xy$ (ii) $9a^2 + 3a^3$
   (b) (i) $2y(2x - y)$ (ii) $3m(m - 4)$
   (c) $x^2 - x$

18. (a) (i) $4x + 17$ (ii) $3x^3 + 5x$
   (b) (i) a^7 (ii) $8x^6y^3$ (iii) $8x^3y^5$

19. (a) $4xy - 2x^2y$ (b) $3pq(2 - q)$ (c) $3m^3$

20. (a) $4xyz^2$ (b) $\dfrac{1}{m^3}$

21. $\dfrac{a^2}{c}$

SECTION 11

Exercise 11   Page 27

1. (a) $x = 5$ (b) $x = 2$ (c) $x = 4$

2. (a) 5   (b) 4

3. (a) $x = 10$ (b) $x = 6$
   (c) $x = 6$ (d) $x = 11$

4. (a) $x = 4$ (b) $x = 6$ (c) $x = 9$

5. (a) $x = 8$ (b) $x = 1$
   (c) $x = -4$ (d) $x = 2.5$

6. (a) $x = 1\frac{1}{3}$ (b) $x = -2$

7. (a) $x = -1.5$ (b) $x = 2.5$
   (c) $x = 0.6$ (d) $x = 1.5$

8. (a) $-5x + 12$ (b) $x = 2.5$

9. (a) $n + (n + 3) + (2n - 1) = 4n + 2$
   (b) $4n + 2 = 30$, $n = 7$

10. (a) $3x + 90 = 285$ (b) 65 pence

11. $x = -2$

12. (a) $x = 7$ (b) $x = 0.6$

13. $x = 5$

14. (a) $(n - 7)$ pence
   (b) $10n + 5(n - 7) = 445$, $n = 32$
     Party hat costs 25 pence.

15. (a) $x^2 - 3x$ (b) $y = -2$

16. (a) $x = 1$ (b) $a = -4$ (c) $x = 6\frac{1}{2}$

17. (a) $x = -3$ (b) $y = -8$

18. (a) $x = 1\frac{2}{5}$ (b) $x = -11$

19. $x = -5$

20. $x = \frac{4}{5}$

21. $x = 8$

SECTION 12

Exercise 12   Page 29

1. (a) 2   (b) -8
   (c) 8   (d) -15

2. (a) (i) 170 (ii) -16
     (iii) No.
       If n is even,
       answer is odd.
   (b) $b = 6$

3. $L = -10$

4. $A = -11$

5. (a) $F = 19$
   (b) $F = 22$

6. 90

7. (a) 18   (b) 32

8. 24

9. $T = -12$

10. $M = 4$

11. $C = 200 - 35n$

12. (a) 40 km
   (b) $K = \dfrac{8M}{5}$
   (c) $M = 37.5$

13. (a) $A = 10$
   (b) $n = \dfrac{c + 5}{10}$

14. $m = \dfrac{n - 3}{p}$

15. $q = \dfrac{5 - 3p}{2}$

16. $n = 14$

17. $r = \dfrac{4C}{3}$

18. (a) $v = 12.2$
   (b) $a = \dfrac{v - u}{t}$

19. $r = \dfrac{ps}{g}$

20. $L = \dfrac{T^2}{4\pi^2} - G$

21. (a) 3 750 000
   (b) $h = \pm\sqrt{\dfrac{5g}{3}}$

22. $b = \dfrac{A - 2wh}{2(w + h)}$

23. $q = \dfrac{5p}{p + 1}$

24. (a) $d = \dfrac{e - 3}{5}$
   (b) $d = \dfrac{4e + 7}{3 - 5e}$

25. $v = \dfrac{uw}{u - w}$

26. $m = \dfrac{3 + 5n}{n - 1}$

SECTION 13

Exercise 13   Page 31

1. (a) 17   (b) 81   (c) $\frac{1}{16}$

2. 37, 60

3. (a) 14
   (b) No. Number must be (multiple of 3) $- 1$.

4. (a) Multiply the last term by 3.
   (b) 405

5. (a) 10, 28
   (b) (i) 2   (ii) Halve the previous term to
               find the next term, etc.
   (c) 46

6. (a) Pattern 20 has 58 squares.
     $3 \times$ (pattern number) -2 (b) $3n - 2$

7. (a) 3, -3 (b) 0   (c) $4n + 1$

8. (a) $2n + 3$ (b) $5n - 4$

9. (a) $88 - 8 = 80$, $80 - 4 = 76$
   (b) $2n - 3$ (c) -3, 0, 5

10. (a) $4n - 1$ (b) $\dfrac{n}{4n - 1}$

11. (a) 38, 51   (b) No common difference.
   (c) The nth term is given by $n^2 + 2$.
     So, $20^2 + 2 = 402$

12. (a) n^2 (b) $n^2 + 3$

SECTION 14

Exercise 14 — Page 34

1. (a) Missing entries are: $-2, 4$

(b)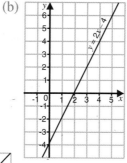

2. (a)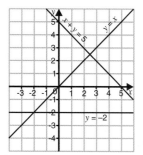

(b) $x + y = 5$

3. Straight line joining $(0, -2)$ and $(5, 13)$.

4. (b) $y = 4$

5. (a) $P(0, 3), Q(6, 0)$ (b) $m = 5.5$

6. (a) $x = 4$ (b) (i) $\frac{1}{2}$ (ii) $y = \frac{1}{2}x + 2$

7. (a)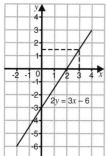

(b) 1.5

(c) $x = 3$

8. 1: **R**,   2: **S**,   3: **Q**,   4: **P**

9. (a) (i) $\frac{1}{2}$ (ii) $y = \frac{1}{2}x + 1$

(b) No.   Gradient of other line is 2.

10. (a) 2   (b) $y = 2x + 6$

11. $y = 0.4x + 130$

12. (a) $y = \frac{2}{5}x + 2$ (b) $y = \frac{2}{5}x - 1$

13. The line $5y = x + 4$ has gradient $\frac{1}{5}$.
The line $y = 6 - 5x$ has gradient -5.
$\frac{1}{5} \times (-5) = -1$, so lines are perpendicular.

14. $y = -2x + 2$

SECTION 15

Exercise 15 — Page 36

1. (a)   (b)

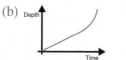

2. (a) 4 minutes   (b) 300 m

(c) Returning home

3. (a) Between 1045 and 1130   (b) 60 km/h

4. (a)

(b) 3.7 km

(c) (i) 36 minutes

(ii) 0754

5. $0.4 \, \text{m/s}^2$

SECTION 16

Exercise 16 — Page 39

1. (a) $x > 3$ (b) $x \geqslant -2$

(c) $x \leqslant 6$ (d) $x > 2$

2. (a)

(b)

(c)

(d)

3. (a) $x \geqslant 3$

(b)

4. (a) $x \leqslant 2$ (b) $x > 3\frac{1}{2}$ (c) $x < -\frac{4}{3}$

5. (a) $-1, 0, 1, 2$ (b) $1, 2$ (c) $-1, 0, 1$

6. $-2, -1, 0, 1, 2, 3, 4$

7. (a) $x \leqslant 2$ (b) $x > -1$ (c) $0, 1, 2$

8. 1: **B**,   2: **C**,   3: **D**,   4: **A**

9. (a) (b)

10. $x \leqslant 20, \quad y \geqslant 5, \quad 2y \leqslant x$

11. $x > 0.6$

12. (a) $-5 \leqslant x < 1$ (b) $n = 0$

13. (a) (i) $x \leqslant 5$ (ii) $x > 2$ (b) 3, 4, 5

SECTION 17

Exercise 17 — Page 41

1. (b) $x = \pm 2.2$ (c) $x = \pm 1.4$

2. (a) Missing entries are: $2, -2, 2$

(b)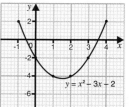

(c) $y = -4.25$

(d) $x = -0.6$ or 3.6

3. (b) (i) $x = 0$ or $x = 5$
   (ii) $x = 0.7$ or $x = 4.3$

4. (a)
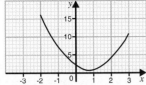

   (b) The graph does not cross the line $y = 0$.
   (c) 0.9, correct to 1 d.p.
5. (a) Missing entries are: 12, 8, 6, 4, 3, 2
   (b)
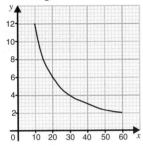
   (c) 3.2 hours
   (d) 26.7 gallons

6. (b) If $y = 3x$ and $y = x^2 + 1$,
      then $3x = x^2 + 1$, which can be
      rearranged as $x^2 - 3x + 1 = 0$.
      Solutions are given by the values of x
      where the two graphs intersect.
   (c) $x = 0.4$ or $x = 2.6$
7. (a) Table of values to draw graph.

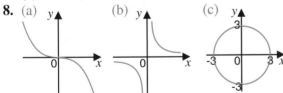

-3	-2	-1	$-\frac{1}{2}$	0	$\frac{1}{2}$	1	2	3
-24	-6	0	0.375	0	-0.375	0	6	24

   (b) $x = 2.3$, correct to 1 d.p.
   (c) $x = 0$, $x = -1$ or $x = 1$
8. (a)   (b)   (c)

9. (a) Table of values to draw graph.

x	-2	-1	0	1	2
y	0.0625	0.25	1	4	16

   (b) $x = 1.5$
10. $x = -3.4$, $y = -2.2$ **and** $x = 3.8$, $y = 1.4$

SECTION 18

Exercise 18   Page 43

1. (a) $\frac{0.6}{0.4} = \frac{9}{6} = \frac{16.5}{11} = 1.5$, so, $m = 1.5n$
   (b) (i) $m = 2.7$ (ii) $n = 8.4$
2. $T = \dfrac{200}{R^2}$
3. $x = 5$
4. (a) $C = 0.025w^2$ (b) $w = 12$
5. (a) $m = \dfrac{2\sqrt{n}}{3}$ (b) (i) $m = 4$ (ii) $n = 225$
6. £16

7. (a) (i) **C**   (ii) **B**   (iii) **E**
   (b) (i) 40   (ii) 160   (iii) 2.5
8. $n = -\frac{1}{3}$

SECTION 19

Exercise 19   Page 45

1. (a) $x^2 - 7x$ (b) $x^2 + 3x - 10$
2. (a) $4x^3 - 3x$ (b) $2x^2 + 5x - 3$
3. (a) $x(x - 4)$ (b) $(x - 3)(x + 5)$
   (c) $(x - 1)(x - 3)$ (d) $(x - 3)(x + 3)$
4. (a) $x = 0$ or $x = -5$
   (b) $x = 3$ or $x = -2$
   (c) $x = -1\frac{1}{2}$ or $x = 1$
5. (a) $4x^2 - 9$
   (b) (i) $x(x + 6)$ (ii) $(x + 2)(x + 4)$
   (c) $x = 3$ or $x = -5$
6. (a) $x = 0$ or $x = -3$ (b) $(x - 3)(x - 4)$
7. (a) $(x - 2)(x - 3)$ (b) $x = 2$ or $x = 3$
8. $(x + 1)(x + 2) = 42$
   $x^2 + 3x + 2 = 42$
   $x^2 + 3x - 40 = 0$
   $(x + 8)(x - 5) = 0$
   $x = -8$ or $x = 5$
9. (a) $(2x + 1)(x - 3)$ (b) $x = -\frac{1}{2}$ or $x = 3$
10. $x = -\frac{2}{3}$ or $x = 1$
11. $x^2 + x - 6 = 0$
12. (a) $(x - 2)^2 - 12$
   (b) $x = -1.46$ or $x = 5.46$
13. $x = -4.19$ or $x = 1.19$
14. $x = -1.19$ or $x = 4.19$
15. $x = -0.78$ or $x = 1.28$
16. $x = 3.4$

SECTION 20

Exercise 20   Page 47

1. (b) $x = \frac{1}{2}$, $y = 3\frac{1}{2}$
2. $x = 2\frac{1}{2}$, $y = \frac{1}{2}$
3. (b) The lines are parallel.
4. $x = \frac{1}{2}$, $y = 4$
5. $x = 3$, $y = -\frac{1}{2}$
6. $x = -2$ $y = 5$
7. $x = 2$, $y = 5$
8. (a) $x + y = 40$ and $4x + 7y = 184$
   (b) $x = 32$, $y = 8$
9. (a) $2x + 4y = 65$ and $x + 3y = 40$
   (b) $x = £17.50$, $y = £7.50$
10. $x = 3$, $y = -2$
11. $x = 5$, $y = -1$
12. (a) $x = 2$, $y = 0$ and $x = -4$, $y = 12$
   (b) $x = 1$, $y = 5$ and $x = 4$, $y = 8$
   (c) $x = 2.24$, $y = 4.48$ and
      $x = -2.24$, $y = -4.48$

13. $x = -2.5$, $y = -2.4$ and $x = 6$, $y = 1$

14. (b) $x = 1$, $y = 2$ **and** $x = -1\frac{1}{2}$, $y = 4\frac{1}{2}$

15. (a) $x = -1$, $y = -12$ and $x = 2$, $y = -9$
 (b) $x = -1$, $y = 4$ and $x = 4$, $y = -1$
 (c) $x = \frac{1}{2}$, $y = 2$ and $x = 1$, $y = 1$

16. $(-7, 1)$ and $(1, 7)$

SECTION 21

Exercise 21   Page 49

1. $12x$

2. $2x(x + y) - (x + y)^2$
 $= 2x^2 + 2xy - x^2 - 2xy - y^2 = x^2 - y^2$

3. (a) $x - 3$ (b) $\frac{x}{2}$ (c) $\frac{x+1}{x-3}$ (d) $\frac{x}{x-1}$

4. (a) $(x + 2y)(x - 2y)$ (b) $\frac{x - 2y}{5}$

5. (a) $\frac{3}{2x}$ (b) $\frac{5x+1}{2(x+1)}$ (c) $\frac{4x-1}{(x+2)(2x-5)}$

6. (a) $\frac{x}{x+3}$ (b) $\frac{x-7}{(x+2)(2x+1)}$

7. (a) $\frac{x-3}{x-2}$ (b) $x = -3$ or $x = \frac{2}{3}$

8. (a) $y = \dfrac{3}{2x-1} - \dfrac{2}{x+3} = \dfrac{3(x+3) - 2(2x-1)}{(2x-1)(x+3)}$

$\qquad = \dfrac{3x+9-4x+2}{2x^2+6x-x-3} = \dfrac{11-x}{2x^2+5x-3}$

 (b) $x = -4.54$ or $x = 1.54$

9. $x = -5.77$ or $x = 2.77$

10. $x = -2\frac{1}{2}$ or $x = 1$

11. (a) (i) $(3x + 1)(x - 3)$ (ii) $\frac{3x-1}{x-3}$
 (b) $x = -2.41$ or $x = 0.41$

12. (a) When $x = 2$, $x^3 - 5x - 8 = -10$
 When $x = 3$, $x^3 - 5x - 8 = 4$
 (b) $x = 2.8$

13. $x = 3.7$

SECTION 22

Exercise 22   Page 51

1. (a) 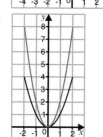 (b)
 (c) (d)

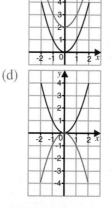

2. (a) 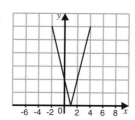 (b)

3. (a) $y = f(2x)$ (b) $y = f(x + 2)$

4. (a) $y = f(x - 2)$ (b) $y = f(x) - 2$
 (c) $y = -f(x)$

5. (a) Table of values to draw graph:

x^2	1	4	9	16	25
y	14	21	37	57	87

 (b) $y = 3x^2 + 10$

Algebra

Non-calculator Paper   Page 52

1. (a) $10x - y$ (b) $35 - 10x$

2. (a) (i) y values are: $-1, 2, 5, 8, 11$
 (b) (i) Missing values are: $-1, 3, 15$
 (ii)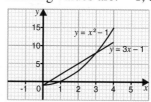

3. (a) $(x - 3)$ years   (b) $4x$ years
 (c) $x + (x - 3) + 4x = 45$, $x = 8$.
 Louisa 5 years,   Hannah 8 years,
 Mother 32 years.

4. $S = -112$

5. (a) 30 minutes   (b) 18 km   (c) 36 km/h

6. (a) (i) $3(a - 2)$ (ii) $k(k - 2)$ (b) £25x

7. (a) $x = 3.5$ (b) $x = 6$ (c) $x = 7$

8. $t = 5$

9. (a) $x^2 + 2x$ (b) $16x + 1$
 (c) (i) $x \geqslant 4.5$
 (ii)

10. (a) $x = 1.5$ (b) $x = 3$

11. 205

12. (a) $300 - x$
 (b) $15x + 10(300 - x) = 3950$, $x = 190$.
 So, 190 people paid £15.

13. (a) $x = 2.5$
 (b) (i) 1, 2, 3, 4   (ii) $x \geqslant 0.6$

14. **A**: **Q**,   **B**: **S**,   **C**: **R**,   **D**: **P**

15. (a) $-3, 1$ (b) $4n - 7$

16. (a) Missing entries are: 4, 1
 (c) (i) $x = 1$ (ii) $x = -0.4$ or 2.4

17.

18. (a) $x = 4.5$ (b) $16x - 6$

19. (a) $x = 3$ (b) $x = 3.5$

20. (a) $\frac{1}{2}$ (b) $\frac{3}{4}$

21. (a) y^5 (b) y^6 (c) y^8

22. (a) $n > 0.6$ (b) $2x^2 + 5x - 3$
  (c) $(x + 1)(x - 4)$ (d) $t = \sqrt{\dfrac{2s}{g}}$

23. (a) (i) $(x - 4)(x - 5)$
    (ii) $x = 4$ or 5
  (b) $x = \frac{1}{2},\ y = -2$

24. (a) (i) $x = 0$ or $x = -2$
    (ii) $y = 1$ or $y = 2$
  (b) $2x^2 + x - 6$

25. (a) $e = \dfrac{8d - 1}{2}$ (b) $x = 2$ or $x = 4$

26. (a) $27x^6y^3$ (b) $2a^4b^2$

27. (a) $3(x - 5)(x + 5)$ (b) $(3x - 5)(x - 1)$

28. $a = \dfrac{7 - 12b}{2}$

29. (a) 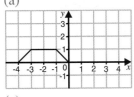 (b)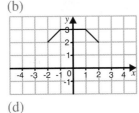

(c) 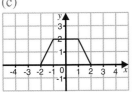 (d)

30. (a) $P = 5\sqrt{q}$ (b) $q = 0.64$

31. (a) $\dfrac{x + 5}{(x - 1)(x + 1)}$ (b) $\dfrac{x + 3}{x + 4}$

32. (a) $(2x + 3)^2 - (2x + 1)^2$
   $= 4x^2 + 12x + 9 - (4x^2 + 4x + 1)$
   $= 8x + 8$
   $= 8(x + 1)$
  (b) $x = -1$ or $x = 9$

33. $y = \dfrac{3x + 5}{x + 1}$

34. (a) $12\,\text{m/s}$ (b) $1.2\,\text{m/s}^2$ (c) $360\,\text{m}$

35. $y = 2x - 7$

36. (a) $\dfrac{a^2 - b^2}{abc}$ (b) ab^2

37. $(-4, -9)$

38. $x = 1,\ y = 3$ and $x = -1\frac{1}{2},\ y = -2$

39. $(2x - 1) - 3(x + 1) = 2(x + 1)(2x - 1)$
   $2x - 1 - 3x - 3 = 4x^2 + 2x - 2$
   $4x^2 + 3x + 2 = 0$

Algebra

Calculator Paper   **Page 55**

1. (a) $(5x + 8y)$ miles (b) 3

2. (a) $m = 3$ (b) $P = 45$

3. (a) 15 minutes (b) $0.75\,\text{km}$
  (c) They increased speed (d) $14\,\text{km/h}$

4. (a) 3 (b) Tom calculated:
       $(2 \times 5)^2 + 1 = 100 + 1 = 101$
     Correct calculation:
       $2 \times 5^2 + 1 = 2 \times 25 + 1 = 51$

5. (a) (i) $a = 3.5$ (ii) $t = -1$
  (b) $x + x - 3 + x + 7 = 25$
       $3x + 4 = 25,\ \ x = 7.$

6. (a) $£(227 + 9n)$
  (b) $227 + 9n = 299,\ \ n = 8$
     Pali worked 8 hours overtime.

7. (b) $P(-5, -9)$

8. (a) (i) $5(2x + 3)$ (ii) $x(x - 3)$
  (b) $x = 1.7$

9. (a) $-2, -9$ (b) $3n + 2$

10. $x = 2.66$

11. (a) Missing entries are: $-1, -4, -1$
  (b) $x = \pm 2.2$

12. (a) $14x + 7$ (b) $L = \dfrac{P - 2W}{2}$

13. (a) $(x + 45)$ pence
  (b) $3(x + 45) + x = 455,\ \ x = 80.$
     Glass of milk costs 80 pence.

14. (a) $x > 3$ (b) $-3, -2$

15. (a) a^7 (b) $t = \dfrac{P - 5}{3}$

16. $x = 4.2$

17. (a) $x = -\frac{1}{5}$ (b) $7x - 3$
  (c) (i) m^6 (ii) n^5

18. (a) **A**: $x = 2$, **B**: $y = 1$, **C**: $x + y = 2$
  (b) $x \leqslant 2,\ \ y \leqslant 1,\ \ x + y \geqslant 2$

19. (a) p^8q^7
  (b) (i) $p^3r^3(r + p^2)$ (ii) $(5p - 2q)(5p + 2q)$
  (c) $r = \pm\sqrt{\dfrac{2p}{3} + 4}$

20. $x = 6.75$

21. (a) $x + y = 2$ (b) $y = x + 2$
  (c) $y = 5x - 10$

22. (a) (i) $40 \times 165 = 6600$ and
         $60 \times 110 = 6600$
    (ii) $f = \dfrac{6600}{L}$ or $fL = 6600$
  (b) $L = 44.9\,\text{cm}$, to 1 d.p.

23. $(2x - 1)(x + 1) = 104$
   $2x^2 + x - 1 = 104$
   $2x^2 + x - 105 = 0$

24. $x = -3.45$ or $x = 1.45$

25. (a) $3x(x + 2) = 4(x + 3)$
       $3x^2 + 6x = 4x + 12$
       $3x^2 + 2x - 12 = 0$
  (b) $x = 1.7$

26. (b) (i) $x = -1.2$ or $x = 1.2$
    (ii) $x = -1.5$ or $x = 1$
  (c) $y = 1 - x$

27. (a) $x = -0.31$ or $x = 4.81$
  (b) $\dfrac{3b - 4}{8 + 5b}$

28. $x = 0.22$ or $x = 2.28$

29. $n = -3$

30. (a) $\dfrac{x+3}{x+1}$ (b) $y = \dfrac{x}{x-1}$

    (c) $a = 4$, $b = 1$, $c = -4$

31. $x = 1$, $y = 3$ and $x = -4$, $y = 8$

32. (a) (i) $a = 9$, $b = -3$ (ii) 2

    (b) $\dfrac{x-1}{x} - \dfrac{x}{x+1} = \dfrac{(x-1)(x+1) - x^2}{x(x+1)}$

$$= \dfrac{x^2 - 1 - x^2}{x(x+1)}$$

$$= \dfrac{-1}{x(x+1)}$$

33. (a) $p = -2$, $q = 3$ (b) $x = \dfrac{3y+1}{y-2}$

34. $x = -1.56$ or $x = 2.56$

SECTION 23

Exercise 23   Page 60

1. $a = 68°$ (supplementary angles)
    $b = 112°$ (corresponding angles)
    $c = 106°$ (allied angles)

2. $x = 36°$

3. (a) $x = 150°$ (b) $y = 123°$ (c) $z = 108°$

4. (a) E.g.   (b) E.g.

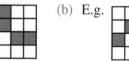

5. $\angle ABC = 114°$

6. (a) $\angle AEB = 36°$
    (b) $\angle EDC = 108°$ (int. $\angle$ regular pentagon)
      $\angle BED = \angle AED - \angle AEB$
      $\angle BED = 108° - 36° = 72°$
      As $\angle EDC + \angle BED = 180°$,   then
      EB is parallel to DC.
      So, $EBCD$ is a trapezium.

7. (a) $\angle ABC = 144°$ (b) $\angle XCY = 108°$

8. $\angle PQX = 151°$

9. 12 sides

10. $140°$

SECTION 24

Exercise 24   Page 62

1. (a) $a = 65°$ (angle in semi-circle = 90°)
    (b) $b = 48°$ (angles in same segment equal)
    (c) $c = 110°$ (angle at centre = 2 × angle
                    at circumference)
    (d) $d = 70°$ (opposite angles of a cyclic
                 quad add to 180°)

2. $x = 67°$, $y = 23°$

3. (a) $\angle ABC \neq 90$ (angle in semi-circle = 90°)
    (b) $\angle ACB = 42°$. $\angle ACB = 180° - 88° - 50°$

4. $a = 100°$, $b = 40°$, $c = 50°$

5. $\angle OQT = \angle OPT = 90°$ (radius meets
                                tangent at 90°)
    $\angle QOP = 360° - (2 \times 90°) - 80° = 100°$
    $\angle PRQ = 50°$ $\left(\angle PRQ = \frac{1}{2}\angle QOP\right)$

6. (a) $\angle ADB = 53°$ (b) $\angle ACD = 32°$
    (c) $\angle ADC = 95°$ (d) $\angle BAD = 95°$

7. $\angle ABC = (x + 90)°$

SECTION 25

Exercise 25   Page 64

1. $17\,\text{cm}^2$

2. (a) $20 \times 10 = 200\,\text{m}^2$
    (b) Bigger, both dimensions rounded up.

3. $27\,\text{cm}^2$

4. $52.5\,\text{cm}^2$

5. $61.7\,\text{cm}$

6. $7\,\text{m}$

7. $86\,\text{cm}^2$

8. $297\,\text{m}^2$

9. $27.5\,\text{m}^2$

10. $45\pi\,\text{cm}^2$

11. $16\pi\,\text{cm}^2$

12. $35.4\,\text{cm}$

13. Yes.   Semi-circle $= \frac{1}{2}(\pi \times 10^2) = 50\pi\,\text{cm}^2$
                Circle $= \pi \times 5^2 = 25\pi\,\text{cm}^2$

14. $25.8\,\text{cm}$

15. $1700\pi\,\text{cm}^2$

16. Area: $39.4\,\text{cm}^2$ Perimeter: $25.3\,\text{cm}$

17. $22.8\,\text{cm}$

SECTION 26

Exercise 26   Page 67

1. (b) (i) $250°$ (ii) $1530\,\text{m}$

2.

3. (a) (b)   **4.** (a) (b)

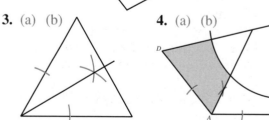

5. (a) (b)

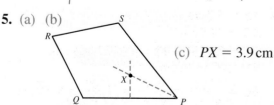

    (c) $PX = 3.9\,\text{cm}$

Exercise 27

1. (a) (i) $x = -1$
   (ii) $\begin{pmatrix} -1 \\ 2 \end{pmatrix}$
   (iii) Centre (0, 2), scale factor 2.
   (b)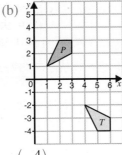

2. (a) Translation with vector $\begin{pmatrix} 4 \\ -3 \end{pmatrix}$.
   (b) Enlargement, scale factor $\frac{1}{3}$, centre (0, 0).
   (c) Enlargement, scale factor -2, centre (0, -1).

3. (a) (i) Reflection in the y axis ($x = 0$).
      (ii) Rotation, through 90° anticlockwise, about (0, 0).
   (b) Rotation, through 180°, about (4, 1).

4. Enlargement, scale factor -2, centre (0, 1).

5. (a) (b)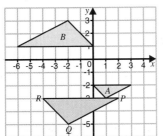
   (c) Enlargement, scale factor -2, centre (0, -1).

Exercise 28

1. $BC = 13\,cm$
2. $PQ = 8\,m$
3. $28.7\,cm$
4. (a) (3, 5)   (b) 7.21 units
5. 8.94 units
6. $3.4^2 = 11.56$ $2.1^2 + 2.8^2 = 12.25$
   Since $3.4^2 < 2.1^2 + 2.8^2$, $\angle PQR < 90°$
   So, ΔPQR is an acute-angled triangle.
7. $48.8\,m$
8. $QR = 7.48\,cm$. Area $\Delta PQR = 18.7\,cm^2$
9. $AC = 10\,cm$
10. $AE = 5.7\,cm$
11. $AB = 22.9\,cm$
12. $TC = \sqrt{(13^2 - 12^2)} = \sqrt{25} = 5\,cm$
    So, $AC = 10\,cm$.
    $BC = \sqrt{\dfrac{AC^2}{2}} = \sqrt{\dfrac{10^2}{2}} = \sqrt{\dfrac{100}{2}} = \sqrt{50}\,cm$

Exercise 29

1. $x = 4.2\,cm$
2. (a) $h = 18.9\,m$
   (b) $x = 50°$
3. (a) $41.6\,cm^2$
   (b) $DC = 8\,cm$
4. $34\,cm$
5. $286°$
6. (a) $XO = 7\,cm$
   (b) $\angle XCO = 51.1°$
7. $18.4°$

Exercise 30

1. (a) 4   (b) 1
2. (a)   (b)
3. (a) **B** has larger volume.
      A: Volume $= 2 \times 6 \times 2 = 24\,cm^3$
      B: Volume $= 3 \times 3 \times 3 = 27\,cm^3$
   (b) **A** has larger surface area.
      A: Surface area $= 56\,cm^2$
      B: Surface area $= 54\,cm^2$
4. $145\,cm^2$
5. $180\pi\,cm^3$
6. $110\,000\,cm^3$
7. (a) $1.9\,m^3$ (b) 1900 litres
8. (a)

   Not full size

   Plan   Elevation F
   (b) $55\,600\,cm^3$
9. (a) $32\,673\,cm^2$
   (b) $10\,cm$
10. $747\,cm^2$
11. (a) $219.8\,cm^2$
    (b) $374\,cm^3$
12. (a) $3811\,cm^3$
    (b) $1143\,cm^2$
13. $11.2\,cm$

Exercise 31

1. $36.25\,km$
2. Debbie is taller.   5 ft 4 in $= 160\,cm$
   Joyce is heavier.   9 st 2 lb $= 58.2\,kg$
3. £813
4. (a) $1.62\,m^2$ (b) $200\,000\,cm^3$
5. $2.45\,kg$
6. $24\,km/h$
7. $\dfrac{\pi a^2}{4} + \dfrac{\pi ac}{2}$ has dimension 2.
8. $68\,cm$
9. Yes.   Maximum sum of weights $< 500\,kg$
   $52.5 + 72.5 + 102.5$
   $\quad + 97.5 + 82.5 + 87.5 = 495\,kg$
10. $13.5 \times 7.5 = 101.25\,m^2$
11. (a) $2.5\,cm \leqslant$ width $< 3.5\,cm$
    (b) $11.25\,cm^2 \leqslant$ area $< 19.25\,cm^2$
    (c) $x = 4$
12. 1142
13. $\dfrac{5.5 + 0.35}{0.35} = 16.714\ldots$

Exercise 32 — Page 80

1. **B** and **D** (ASA)
2. (a) Ratio of widths $= 1 : 2$ **but**
   ratio of lengths $= 5 : 7$.   (b) 7.5 cm
3. (a) $x = 7.8$ cm   (b) $y = 4.3$ cm
4. (a) $1 : 50$ (b) 560 cm²
5. (a) $4 : 9$ (b) 40 cm³
6. (a) 2 kg   (b) 22 500 cm²

SECTION 33

Exercise 33 — Page 82

1. (a) $\overrightarrow{XY} = \mathbf{y} - \mathbf{x}$ (b) $\overrightarrow{QP} = \frac{1}{2}(\mathbf{x} - \mathbf{y})$
2. (a) $\overrightarrow{AB} = \begin{pmatrix} 6 \\ -4 \end{pmatrix}$ (b) $D(2, 6)$
3. (a) $\overrightarrow{AD} = 3\mathbf{q}$ (b) $\overrightarrow{CD} = 2\mathbf{q} - \mathbf{p}$
4. (a) (i) $\overrightarrow{OC} = 2\mathbf{a}$ (ii) $\overrightarrow{AB} = 3\mathbf{b} - 3\mathbf{a}$
   (iii) $\overrightarrow{CD} = 2\mathbf{b} - 2\mathbf{a}$
   (b) AB is parallel to CD, $2\overrightarrow{AB} = 3\overrightarrow{CD}$.
5. (a) (i) $\overrightarrow{OE} = 2\mathbf{a} + \mathbf{c}$ (ii) $\overrightarrow{AC} = \mathbf{c} - \mathbf{a}$
   (iii) $\overrightarrow{OF} = \frac{1}{3}(2\mathbf{a} + \mathbf{c})$
   (b) O, F and E are colinear, $\overrightarrow{OE} = 3\overrightarrow{OF}$.
6. (a) (i) $\overrightarrow{OQ} = \frac{1}{2}(\mathbf{a} + \mathbf{b})$
   (ii) $\overrightarrow{OM} = \frac{1}{3}(\mathbf{a} + \mathbf{b})$
   (iii) $\overrightarrow{PB} = \mathbf{b} - \frac{1}{2}\mathbf{a}$
   (iv) $\overrightarrow{PM} = \frac{1}{3}\left(\mathbf{b} - \frac{1}{2}\mathbf{a}\right)$
   (b) M lies on the line PB, $\overrightarrow{PM} = \frac{1}{3}\overrightarrow{PB}$.

SECTION 34

Exercise 34 — Page 85

1. (a) (i) $x = 300°$ (ii) $x = 120°, 240°$
   (b) (i) graph   (ii) $x = 45°, 225°$
   $y = \cos x$
   $y = \sin x$
2. $099.7°$ (or $100°$)
3. $h = 13.4$ m
4. $CD = 4.4$ cm
5. (a) $\angle QRP = 28.6°$ (b) 103 cm²
6. (a) $AB = 52.5$ km (b) $338°$
7. $ZY = 11.8$ km. Bearing of Z from $Y = 282°$.
8. (a) $\angle BAC = 62.7°$ or $\angle BAC = 117.3°$
   (b) $BC = 12.9$ cm

Non-calculator Paper — Page 86

1. (a) 18 cm²   (b) 25 cm²
2. $140° + 40° = 180°$, so, allied angles.
   So, AB is parallel to CD.
3. (a) (i) 2400 cm³ (ii) 2.4 litres (b) 5 cm
4. (b) $308°$
5.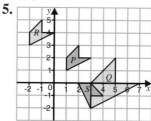
6. (a) $x = 52°$ (b) $y = 85°$ (c) $z = 21°$
7. (diagram)
8. 3.6 cm
9. 14π cm
10. 2.25 m
11. (a) abc has dimension 3 (volume).
    (b) πa **and** $\sqrt{a^2 - c^2}$ **and** $2(a + b + c)$
12. (a) (i) $x = \sqrt{3^2 + 4^2} = \sqrt{9 + 16} = \sqrt{25} = 5$
    (ii) 174 m²
    (b) $y = 8$ m
13. (a) (i) $x = 5.1$ cm, $y = 4.7$ cm
    (ii) Match corresponding angles.
    $50°$ angle is bounded by 5.1 cm (x)
    and 4.7 cm (y).
    (b) Yes. Both right-angled triangles.
    Hypotenuse: $PQ = 4 \times AB$
    Side: $QR = 4 \times AC$
    So, ΔPQR is an enlargement of
    ΔABC, scale factor 4.
14. 10 sides
15. $x = 105°$ (alt. angles)
    $y = 75°$ (opp. $\angle$'s cyclic quad add to $180°$)
16. (a) $AC = 4.8$ cm (b) $AE = 2.8$ cm
17. (a) (i) $\frac{4}{5}$ (ii) $\frac{3}{5}$
    (b) $XY = 12.5$ cm, $YZ = 7.5$ cm
18. (a) $\begin{pmatrix} 0 \\ 9 \end{pmatrix}$
    (b) (i) $\overrightarrow{XQ} = 3\mathbf{p}$ (ii) $\overrightarrow{QP} = -4\mathbf{p}$
    (c) $\overrightarrow{AM} = \overrightarrow{NC} = \frac{1}{2}\mathbf{a}$ (AB parallel to DC, given)
    $\overrightarrow{AN} = \mathbf{b} + \frac{1}{2}\mathbf{a}$ and $\overrightarrow{MC} = \frac{1}{2}\mathbf{a} + \mathbf{b}$
    So, AN is equal and parallel to AC.
    Hence, $AMCN$ is a parallelogram.
19. 486π cm³
20. (a) Coordinates of object:
    $(3, 6), (15, 6), (15, 12), (12, 15), (3, 12)$
    (b) 9 times bigger.

21. (a)

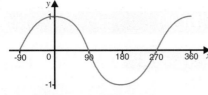

(b) $\cos 210° = -0.866$

(c) $x = -60°, 60°$ and $300°$

22. (a) $AD = BC$ (opp. sides of parallelogram)

$DQ = AB$ (given, AB and CD are opp. sides of parallelogram and P and Q are midpoints)

$\angle ADQ = \angle PBC$ (opp. $\angle$'s of parallelogram)

So, ΔPBC and ΔQDA congruent, SAS.

(b) AP parallel to QC (given)

$AP = QC$ (given, P and Q are midpoints AB and DC)

So, $APCQ$ is a parallelogram.

Hence, AQ is parallel to PC.

23. 8π cm²

Shape, Space, Measures

Section Review

Calculator Paper   Page 89

1. (a) E.g.   (b) E.g.

2. (a) E.g.

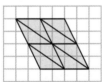

(b) No.   Only equilateral triangles, squares and hexagons tessellate.
Interior angle must divide into 360° a whole number of times.

3. (a) (i)   (ii) 46 cm²

(b) 2.5 cm

4. (a) (i) $x = 41°$
(ii) $y = 139°$ (supplementary angles)
(b) (i) $z = 142°$ (allied angles)
(ii) 147.5 cm²

5. 50.3 cm²   **6.** E.g.

7. (a) Ext. $\angle = \frac{360°}{6} = 60°$.
a = int. $\angle = 180° - 60° = 120°$
(b) $b = 15°$

8. 21.5 km

9. (a)

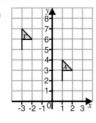

(b) (i) Enlargement, scale factor 2, centre (0, 0).
(ii) Rotation, 90° clockwise, about (3, 2).

10. (a) 41 m²   (b) (i) $AB = 5$ m   (ii) 30 m

11. Footpaths HX, XS, shorter by 171 m.
Footpaths 850 m,   Waverly Crescent 1021 m.

12. 280 000 cm³

13. (a) 122°   (b) $AB = 18.5$ km

14. (a) $\angle PSR = 129°$ (opp. $\angle$'s of cyclic quad sum to 180°)
(b) $\angle PRS = 32°$ (alternate segment)

15. (a)

(b) Enlargement, scale factor $-\frac{1}{2}$, centre $(-1, 2)$.

16. (a) 74.4 cm²   (b) 2.43 cm

17. (a) $\overrightarrow{OX} = 2\mathbf{b}$, $\overrightarrow{AX} = 2\mathbf{b} - \mathbf{a}$.

(b) $\overrightarrow{BM} = \mathbf{b} - \frac{1}{2}(2\mathbf{b} - \mathbf{a}) = \frac{1}{2}\mathbf{a}$

$\overrightarrow{OA} = \mathbf{a}$ and $\overrightarrow{BM} = \frac{1}{2}\mathbf{a}$

(multiples of the same vector, $\mathbf{a}$)

So, BM is parallel to OA.

18. (a) $DF = 36$ cm   (b) 21.2°

19. (a) $AC = 7.5$ cm   (b) $\angle ABC = 49°$
(c) $AB = 9.1$ cm

20. (a) 1.1 m³   (b) 0.326 m³

21. $BC = 10.9$ cm

22. Upper bound = 4.7782… cm
Lower bound = 4.7186… cm

SECTION   35

Exercise 35   Page 92

1. E.g. Students from one year group only. All students from the same class. More/less homework may be set on different nights.

2. E.g. Leading question.
Question has more than one part.

3. E.g. Two thirds of men were over 45.
All women are aged 16 to 45.
Twice as many women as men.

4. No.   Men: $\frac{180}{200} = 90\%$ Women: $\frac{240}{300} = 80\%$
Higher proportion of men can drive.

5. (a) 2   (b) Yes.   21 people have cats **and** 17 people have dogs.
(c) 25 dogs

6. (a) E.g. Sample could be boys (girls) only.
Sample could be all younger pupils.
(b) E.g. Divide school population into year groups and each group into boys and girls.
Choose, at random, pupils from each group in proportion to size of group.

7.

Year group	7	8	9	10	11
Sample	22	24	18	20	16

1. (a) £9   (b) £10.50   (c) £11.50
   (d) Median. Mode is the lowest price and mean is affected by the one higher-priced meal.
2. E.g. Right: Class B   median 61%
                Class A   median 58%
      Wrong: Class B   mean   57.9%
                Class A   mean   58.5%
3. 99.5 kg
4. (a) 5   (b) 9
   (c) Reg: mean;   Reg 9,   Helen 8.6
        Helen: mode;   Reg 9,   Helen 10
        Friend: median;   Reg 9,   Helen 9
5. (a) (i) 1   (ii) 3   (iii) 3.35
   (b) Mode **and** median
6. (a) £23.20
   (b) The calculation is based on the average for each class interval, which is at the centre of the class.

1. (a) 12   (b) 22°C   (c) 14°C
   (d) 5°C or 24°C. Temperature can be either 2°C above previous maximum, or 2°C below previous minimum.
2. (a) (i) *C*   (ii) *A*   (iii) *B*   (b) *C*
3. (a)

Sport	Soccer	Rugby	Cricket	Basketball	Other
Angle	148°	50°	36°	74°	52°

   (b) 21 girls
4. (a)

```
1 | 0  means 10 text messages
0 | 2 3 5 5 7 9
1 | 0 1 2 3 5 7        (b) 19
2 | 0 1
```

5. (a) 53.3%   (b) 7 : 11
   (c)

Injury	Fatal	Serious	Minor	None
Angle	16°	36°	116°	192°

6. (a)

```
  Boys   |   Girls   2 | 5 means 2.5 cm
         | 2 | 5
     5 5 | 3 | 0 5 5 5
 5 5 5 0 0 | 4 | 0 5 5
     0 0 | 5 | 0 5
```

   (b) Girls have more variation in their estimates. Range: girls 3 cm, boys 1.5 cm
7. (b) Negative correlation. Members who spend longer on exercise each day tend to have a lower resting pulse rate.
   (d) Estimate would be beyond known values.

1. (a) (c)

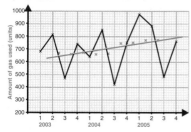

   (b) 675, 665, 675, 662.5, 665, 747.5, 755, 772.5, 775
   (d) Slight increase in units used.
2.

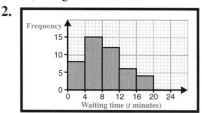

3. Vertical scale does not begin at zero. Bars are different widths.
4. (a) $80 \leqslant age < 90$ (b) 40
   (c) (ii) Women:

Age (a years)	Frequency
$60 \leqslant a < 70$	1
$70 \leqslant a < 80$	5
$80 \leqslant a < 90$	13
$90 \leqslant a < 100$	6

   (iii) More men under 80 than women. Only women aged over 90. Women have greater range of ages.
5. 50 people.
6. Frequency densities: 18, 52, 7, 3

1. (a) (i) 66 m   (ii) 16 m
   (b)

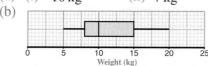

2. (a) (i) 10 kg   (ii) 7 kg
   (b)

3. (a) £450   (b) £100
   (c) The average price paid for a computer is much higher than for a television. Computers have a smaller variation in price than televisions.

Page 106
Page 108

4. (a) 260 g (b) Cooking apples (c) 180 g
   (d) The average weight of cooking apples is larger and they have a greater variation in weight than eating apples.

5. (a) Cumulative frequencies: 5, 29, 62, 90, 100
   (b) 5.2 hours
   (c) At 4.2 hours, cumulative frequency is 33. At 6.2 hours, cumulative frequency is 65. So, 32 people spent within 1 hour of median time on the Internet.

SECTION 40

Exercise 40

1. (a)

G	B	C
G	C	B
B	G	C
B	C	G
C	B	G
C	G	B

   (b) (i) $\frac{7}{20}$ (ii) 0.6

2. (a) 0.1 (b) 0.7

3. (a) $\frac{5}{12}$ (b) $\frac{5}{11}$

4. (a) $\frac{9}{20} = 0.45$
   (b) 2, 3, 3, 4, 5. Numbers 2, 3, 4, 5 have occurred and 3 has occurred twice as often as other numbers.
   (c) 100. Relative frequency of 5 is $\frac{1}{5}$. $\frac{1}{5} \times 500 = 100$

5. (a) HHH, HHT, HTH, THH
       THT, HTT, TTH, TTT   (b) $\frac{3}{8}$

6. (a)

   (b) 0.28 (c) 0.54

7. (a) (i)
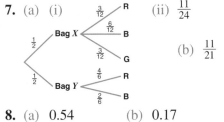
   (ii) $\frac{11}{24}$
   (b) $\frac{11}{21}$

8. (a) 0.54 (b) 0.17

Handling Data

Section Review

Non-calculator Paper

1.

Pantomime	Angle
Aladdin	135°
Cinderella	105°
Jack and the Bean Stalk	75°
Peter Pan	45°

2. (a)

Second dice

×	1	2	3	4	5	6
1	1	2	3	4	5	6
2	2	4	6	8	10	12
3	3	6	9	12	15	18
4	4	8	12	16	20	24
5	5	10	15	20	25	30
6	6	12	18	24	30	36

(First dice labels the rows.)

   (b) (i) $\frac{1}{36}$ (ii) $\frac{6}{36} = \frac{1}{6}$ (iii) 0

3. (a)

4 | 5 means 4.5 cm

4	5 8 8
5	0 0 4 4 5 8
6	0 2 4 5 5 5 6 8
7	0 2 4

   (b) 2.9 cm

4. E.g. Leading question.
   Question has more than one part.

5. (c) (i) 2 (ii) 5
   (b) The next 25-week period had more variation in the number of accidents per week, but a lower weekly average.

6. (a)

First	N	N	N	N	N	N
Second	A	A	R	R	C	C
Third	R	C	A	C	R	A
Fourth	C	R	C	A	A	R

   (b) $\frac{1}{3}$

7. (c) (i) 38 miles
   (ii) 80 miles is beyond the range of recorded data.

8. (a) $\frac{17}{75}$
   (b) Yes. Female: $\frac{12}{50} = 24\%$
       Male: $\frac{5}{25} = 20\%$

9. (a) 110 cm - 120 cm (b) 118.5 cm

10. (a)

   (b) (i) 0.42 (ii) 0.46

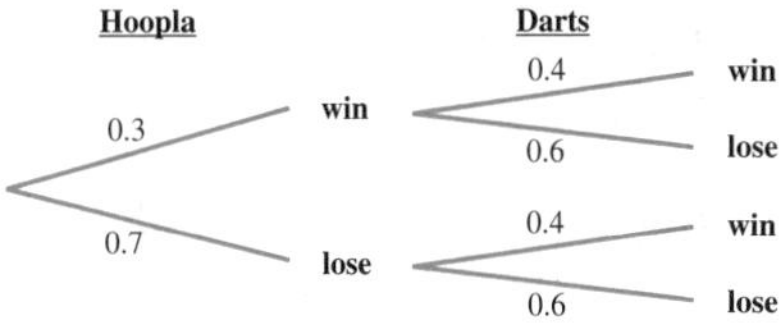

11. (a) (ii) Median = 28 minutes, Interquartile range = 11 minutes
    (b) Median = 45 minutes, Interquartile range = 8 minutes
    (c) Times for male students have lower average and more variation than those for female students.

12. (a) E.g. Sample not representative of all ages. Older pupils are more likely to have a mobile phone.
Use of phone may vary with age.
    (b) (i) Take 10% of boys and 10% of girls from each year group, each sample being selected at random.
       (ii) Ensure boys and girls from each year group are represented in proportion to their numbers.

13. (a) 0.46
    (b) The probability of rain in each town is independent.

14. (a) 90   (b) (i) 15.1%   (ii) 21.7 m

15. (a) (i) 0.28   (ii) 0.48   (b) 0.1

Handling Data

Calculator Paper   Page 111

1. (a) **X 1, X 3, Y 1, Y 3**
    (b) Numbers 1 and 3 are not equally likely.

2. (a) $\frac{3}{20}$ (b) $\frac{7}{20}$

3. (a)

Activity	Paid job	Doing homework	In bed	Sport	Other
Angle	130°	43°	90°	83°	14°

    (b) (i) Similar proportion of students doing paid jobs.
       (ii) Higher proportion of Year 11 stay in bed than Year 13.

4. 56.7 kg

5. (a) (i) 2   (ii) 1.9   (b) (i) 0.75   (ii) 12

6. 72

7. (b) Circle point (2.5, 10)
    (c) Negative correlation, fairly strong.
    (d) (ii) 9.5 km

8. (a) 178.5 seconds
    (b) $150 < t \leqslant 180$
There are 40 tracks, and the 20th and 21st times occur within the class interval.
    (c) $\frac{3}{40}$

9. (a) (ii) Median = 1.6 km, IQR = 1.1 km
    (b)

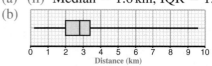

    (c) The average distance for primary pupils is less and they have less variation in the distances travelled.

10. £75, £93

11. (a)

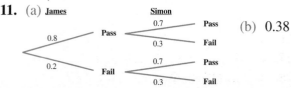

    (b) 0.38

12. (a) (i) 0.2   (ii) 0.4   (b) (i) 0.0625 (ii) 0.12

13. (a) Frequency densities: 2.5, 4.2, 2.4, 0.6
    (b) 13.6 minutes   (c) 6

14. (a)

Age (y years)	Sample
$16 \leqslant y < 25$	22
$25 \leqslant y < 40$	33
$40 \leqslant y < 60$	28
$60 \leqslant y < 65$	17

    (b) E.g. Employees within each age group are represented in proportion to their numbers.

15. (a) $\frac{4}{25}$ (b) $\frac{23}{50}$

Exam Practice

Non-calculator Paper   Page 114

1. (a) 3500   (b) $50 \times 300 = 15\,000$

2. $(-1, 1)$

3. (a) $a = -1$ (b) $m = \frac{2}{3}$ (c) $a = 4$

4. (a) $\frac{1}{8}$ (b) $\frac{4}{8} = \frac{1}{2}$ (c) $\frac{5}{8}$

5. (a)

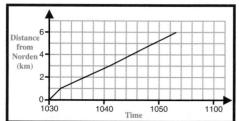

    (b) Between Norden and Corfe Castle.
    (c) Times and distances are joined by straight lines to show average speed.

6. 5 cm

7. (a) $\frac{17}{20}$ (b) Beth £60, Lucy £20

8. (a) $x + (2x - 1) + 3x = 41$
    (b) $x = 7$ Numbers on cards: 7, 13, 21

9. (a) $x = 70°$ (alternate angles)
    (b) $\angle APQ = \angle ARS = 60°$
$\angle PAQ = 180° - (60° + 70°) = 50°$
$y = 50°$, as $y = \angle PAQ$ (vert. opp. $\angle$'s)

10. $3n - 1$

11. (a) (i) Enlargement, scale factor $\frac{1}{2}$, centre $(0, 1)$.
       (ii) Rotation, 90° anticlockwise, about $(1, -1)$.
    (b)

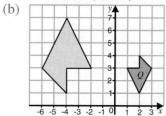

12. (a) 1 : 8   (b) 1.12 m
    (c) Greatest: 21.5 cm, least: 20.5 cm

13. $V = 3 \times 4 \times 4 \times 8 = 384 \text{ cm}^3$

14. (a) $3(2x + 5)$ (b) $x = 8.5$

15. (a) (b)

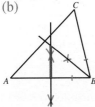

16. $\sqrt{a^2 + b^2}$ and $4(a + b + c)$
Both have dimension 1.

17. 2.3×10^7

18. (a) $x^2 + x - 30$
  (b) (i) $(x - 4)(x - 6)$ (ii) $\dfrac{x - 6}{x + 4}$

19. (a) $a = 36$ (b) $c = \pm\sqrt{\dfrac{a}{b}}$

20. (a) Missing entries are: $2, -2, 2$
  (c) $y = -4.25$ (d) $x = -0.6$ or 3.6
  (e) Draw the line $y = x$
    $x = -0.45$ or 4.45

21. (a) $x = 105°$, $\angle ADC + x = 180°$, so,
    $x = 105°$
  (b) No. $\angle BAD + \angle ADC = 175°$
    If parallel, $\angle BAD + \angle ADC = 180°$

22. (a) (i) $8pq^3$ (ii) $3x - y$ (b) $\dfrac{8}{343}$

23. (a) $y = x^2 - 1$ (b) $y = 2^x$
  (c) $x^2 + y^2 = 9$ (d) $y = \dfrac{1}{x}$

24. (a) $\overrightarrow{ST} = \mathbf{b} - \mathbf{a}$, $\overrightarrow{RA} = \frac{1}{2}\,\mathbf{a}$, $\overrightarrow{AB} = \frac{1}{2}(\mathbf{b} - \mathbf{a})$
  (b) AB is parallel to ST and half its length.

25. (a) $(n - 3)^2 - 2(n - 3)$
    $= n^2 - 6n + 9 - 2n + 6$
    $= n^2 - 8n + 15 = (n - 3)(n - 5)$
  (b) $x = 2$ or $x = -5$

26. (a) $\dfrac{2\sqrt{2}}{5}$ (b) $2\sqrt{3}$

27. (a) $\dfrac{2x}{x + 3}$ (b) $m = \dfrac{np}{n - p}$
  (c) $x = 1$, $y = 2$ and $x = 4$, $y = \frac{1}{2}$

28. (a)

```
y
1          ⌒          y = cos x
  \      /   \      /
0  90  180  270  360   x
        \___/
-1
```

  (b) (i) $x = 113.6°$, $246.4°$
    (ii) $x = 41.4°$, $318.6°$

29. (a) $N = 0.5\dot{7}\dot{7}$
    $100N = 57.5\dot{7}\dot{7}$
    $99N = 57.5\dot{7}\dot{7} - 0.5\dot{7}\dot{7}$
    $99N = 57$
  (b) $\dfrac{57}{990}$

30. $\dfrac{31}{66}$

31. (b) (i) 4.9 (ii) $x = 3.8$

Calculator Paper   **Page 117**

1. (a) 0.78
  (b) 0.3, $\frac{8}{25}$, 33%, $\frac{1}{3}$

2. (a) **150 g**   (b) **100 g**

3. (a) $1260°$
  (b) $a = 33°$, $b = 32°$, $c = 65°$

4. (a) (i) $x^2 - 3x$ (ii) $13y + 5$
  (b) (i) $3(2a + 3)$ (ii) $b(2b + 1)$
  (c) (i) $x = 100$ (ii) $x = -4.5$

5. (b) 2.15 km, $295°$

6. 27%

7. (a) $5 < w \leqslant 10$ (b) $\frac{54}{65}$
  (d) 9.2 kg

8. (a) 7.35 cm^2 (b) 72.03 cm^3
  (c) 6.94 g/cm^3

9. $x = 3.8$

10. 61.1%

11. 312 (or 310)

12. (a) -2, -1, 0, 1 (b) $x < \frac{1}{2}$

13. (a) 1.5×10^8 km
  (b) 393.7
  (c) 1.25×10^9 km

14. (a) 7.2 km   (b) $124°$

15. (a) $x = 2.5$ (b) $x = 5$, $y = -1$

16. (a) £2166.41 (b) £58

17. 1.4 cm

18. (a) $y(15 - y) = 55$
      $15y - y^2 = 55$
    $y^2 - 15y + 55 = 0$
  (b) 8.62 cm by 6.38 cm

19. (a) $a = 0.1$, $b = 2.4$
  (b) The spring is 2.4 cm in length.
  (c) $l = 15.9$ cm
    The spring extends at a constant rate.

20. (a) 65.4 cm^3 (b) 10.9 cm

21. (a) $6x^2 - 7xy - 5y^2$
  (b) $ab(4a + b)$
  (c) $r = \dfrac{h(2 + y)}{(y - 2)}$

22. Frequency densities are: $0.46, 0.32, 0.16, 0.01$

23. (a) $a = 4$, $b = 40$
  (b) -40
  (c) $x = -10.3$ or 2.3

24. $051°$

25. $(x + 1)^2 - (x^2 + 1)$
    $= x^2 + 2x + 1 - x^2 - 1$
    $= 2x$

26. (a) $k = 3$, $n = 2$ (b) $p = 7$

27. $x = 6.5$, $y = -1.5$ and $x = 1$, $y = 4$

28. (a) $\angle PQR = 60°$ (b) 42.2 cm^2

Index ●●●●●●●●●●●●●●●●●●●●●●●●●●●●●●●●●

136